PERSPECTIVES ON
POVERTY
AND
HEALTH
CARE

A Collection
of Readings

JEANNE M. BURGER
EDITOR

■Precedent Press■

■Precedent Press■

ISBN: ISBN0-9763088-2-7

Direct correspondence and permission requests to:
　　E-mail:　　orders@precedentpress.org
　　Web site:　www.precedentpress.org
　　Mail:　　　Precedent Press
　　　　　　　9465 Counselors Row, Suite 200
　　　　　　　Indianapolis, Indiana 46240
　　Telephone:　317-348-4118

Design and layout: Todd Giles of TAGdesign Studios — www.tagdesignstudios.com

To my parents, Gene and Marty Burger, who are truly capable of making a place in the community for anyone.

Jeanne

Introduction

"Perspectives on Poverty and Health Care" is a selection of readings that explore one of the most significant issues affecting our health care systems and our world today. There are many dimensions to poverty that impact the poor and those who seek to provide them with adequate care. Individuals who gain new insights and perspectives on important aspects of poverty will be in the best position to bring about positive and effective change regarding poverty in their communities.

The material in this reader looks at the causes, effects, and challenges of poverty from the perspectives of politics, policy, culture, ethics, economics, faith, justice and community. I particularly focused on helping readers connect with the poor and find real and meaningful solutions to poverty. The questions, case studies, and scenarios that accompany each article are designed to stimulate group discussion and critical thinking.

The content of this book is relevant firstly to nurses, but it is pertinent to professionals working in any aspect of health care, those who interact with the health care system in any way, such as pastors and priests, or anyone with a concern for the poor.

I wish to thank Barb Schulz, MS, RN, who had the vision for this work, Dr. John Johnson, who has provided invaluable mentoring and support throughout the process of bringing this reader to publication, and each of the contributing authors who have shared their hearts, time and expertise to help us all better understand poverty and the capacities of the poor. Special thanks go to the members of New Life Lutheran Church, Ft. Wayne, Indiana, for encouraging me and praying for the outcome of this book.

Jeanne Burger, MSN, RN
General Editor

Table of Contents

A Place in the Community

by Jeanne M. Burger

Summary: The cycle of poverty and ill health disheartens the poor and leads to feelings of powerlessness, worthlessness, and vulnerability. This article identifies ways to transform the lives of the poor by recognizing their capabilities and involving them in finding unique solutions to their own problems.

People living in poverty are considered a vulnerable population, which, by formal definition, means they are susceptible, at risk, neglected, capable of being wounded or harmed, and face real or perceived threats to health and life (Rogers 1997; Malone 2000; Daniel 1998; Mirow 2003). But Maxine[1], who is struggling against poverty and homelessness, would simply explain it this way, "I know what I am capable of, but I can't do it. I feel vulnerable because everyone else controls my life."

When asked about her situation, Maxine doesn't focus on her lack of income, meager living situation or limited possessions. The thing that bothers her most is that she seldom feels like a valuable human being anymore. Maxine worked for thirty years, often at jobs that involved hard, physical labor; she made enough income to raise her son alone. Then the hard labor took its toll and she got sick, which led to the loss of her job, health insurance, and feeling of self-worth. More than anything, Maxine would like to feel that her life has meaning and

purpose, but to her, it seldom does. She has said, "The only place I feel whole is at church. That's the only place where people care about me and treat me human."

Davis (1990) relates similar inhuman feelings from her own childhood experience with poverty. "The main problem was not belonging—not belonging anywhere or with anyone. I didn't even consider myself a real person." In one memory, she ran after a truck from which a man was throwing bread onto the ground, just so she could have some decent food. She writes, "I'm glad there were people compassionate enough to feed the poor. But how I hated that bakery! I despised the man who stood up there and threw me bread. I despised him because I had to trade my dignity, *myself*, for a loaf of bread" (¶ 7-9).

Like Maxine, people around the world who live in poverty experience feelings of worthlessness, exclusion, powerlessness,

> In spite of their feelings of inadequacy, poor people are full of potential...and they long for a meaningful place in the community.

Jeanne M. Burger MSN, RN, CCRN, is an adjunct faculty member at Indiana Wesleyan University. She holds a degree in Community Health Nursing, has experience in critical care nursing and has worked cross-culturally with refugees from many nations. She is also a freelance writer.

shame, and vulnerability (Dodd & Munck 2002). Knowing this, the question we must ask is: What are we, as health care professionals, willing to do to help Maxine and the millions of people like her overcome the overwhelming hopelessness and despair that arise because of their poverty?

According to the International Council of Nurses:

> For those living in poverty the impact reaches far beyond income and monetary matters: the greatest adversities are the lost opportunities to develop essential human capabilities. Poverty is a disease that saps people's energy, dehumanizes them and creates a sense of helplessness and loss of control over one's life. (ICN n.d., ¶ 1)

The cry of the poor that reaches beyond financial need is a cry for love, and genuine caring and belonging. It is not a cry for more handouts. Most poor people would agree that a constant stream of handouts only demeans them. They would rather work, but often their health won't allow it or work is quite hard to find.

More than a decade ago, an experienced community organizer named John McKnight spoke out against serving the poor in dehumanizing ways. He called for us, instead, to "find another's gifts, contributions and capacities," adding, "Use them. Give them a place in the community" (McKnight 1995, 15). I believe this idea, to "give them a place in the community," is a significant one on which we must center our efforts to truly help the poor.

In spite of their feelings of inadequacy, poor people are full of gifts and potential, and are usually quite capable of becoming involved in resolving their own problems. They long for a meaningful place in the community. Unfortunately, we often over-

> Poverty is a disease that saps people's energy, dehumanizes them and creates a sense of helplessness and loss of control over one's life.

look the abilities of poor people; we emphasize their deficiencies, offering services for those deficiencies and "doing for" them rather than focusing on their capacities and allowing them to "do for themselves." This robs them of dignity.

The purpose of this article is to identify ways that nurses and other health care workers can address issues of powerlessness, worthlessness, and vulnerability among the poor by offering them renewed hope that they are valuable people who can make valid contributions and have meaningful places in their communities. Some important ways we can do this are by encouraging participation and building capacities, by recognizing our mutual vulnerability, by listening, and by viewing the poor as Jesus did.

Participation: Building Capacities

Nurses who encourage and empower the poor to participate in defining and solving their own problems acknowledge that poor people are unique individuals of value and worth. Programs that build on the deficiencies rather than the capacities of people in need tend to encourage dependency on systems and professionals instead of encouraging people to tap into their own gifts and potential. More service systems are probably not the best answers for meeting the needs of the poor, because too often those services promote and fund the service providers instead of promoting the abilities of poor people. Service systems actually exploit the poor when they create income for those who serve without effectively creating income for the poor. The very services that claim to help the poor often perpetuate their need for those services and demoralize the poor in the process (McKnight 1995).

Provider-focused approaches usually define the poor in terms of their problems—illiterate, unemployed, or homeless—rather than in terms of their abilities—organizer, decorator, or builder. A better and more effective approach to reversing poverty says, "We have some resilient, creative people here who have some problems, but who also are capable, with the right support, of getting involved and finding unique solutions to their own problems." This capacity-focused approach may take longer to implement than standard approaches because it takes time to get to know people and their gifts and to walk beside them as they take steps forward out of poverty. But the effects can be longer-lasting than a repetitive succession of services.

We must give priority to poverty-reversing strategies that focus energy and funds on issues and projects such as job creation, work skills, planting healthy gardens, child care, or the development of small businesses. These are more likely to break the cyclical link between poverty and poor health, and to combat feelings of worthlessness, powerlessness, and vulnerability among the poor. Focusing on capabilities has the potential to improve current and future conditions in poverty-stricken communities (ICN n.d.; McKnight 1995; Taylor 1973). The question is: Do we, as health care providers, have the will to do this?

Building on people's capacities often requires some changed thinking or adaptation on our part, but it is possible. McKnight (1995) tells the story of a small early-twentieth-century community that had a large population of deaf people and no special services for them, yet the deaf in that small community were as successful as the hearing in every measurable way. Thirty miles away, in a community that had all kinds of specialized services, the deaf led much poorer quality lives. The difference was that people in the smaller town didn't consider deafness a deficiency. Instead, everyone in the town learned sign language so that deaf people could be fully integrated into the community. The members of the town adapted themselves so everyone could have a place in their community.

One of the most important keys to successful transformation in the lives of the poor is the incorporation of the poor into the process of transformation. For example, The World Bank promotes programs that "give priority to strengthening the local groups' organizational capacities to identify priority needs and to manage development projects" (The World Bank Group "From *Voices* to Action" n.d.). Outreach International, an organization that has worked for decades on human and community development around the world observes that, "…when the poor are intimately involved in their own development, the results are long lasting…when people work together to resolve the problems of poverty, hope is born and lives are transformed" (Outreach International 2005c, ¶ 5). These international leaders recognize the value of building on people's capacities.

> *…when people work together to resolve the problems of poverty, hope is born and lives are transformed.*

No one wants to be constantly on the receiving end of service. I learned this valuable lesson when homeless women began coming to my church's regular midweek meal and fellowship. At first, many of us found great joy and took great pride in helping to prepare, serve and clean up the meal, with little regard for the results of our service on those served. The women and their children were present, but were not a real part of our community. Then, for a time, we didn't have enough servers, which is when the homeless women were kind enough to become our servers—and our teachers. They grabbed spoons, served food, washed tables, swept floors, and left the building with their heads held high and a new light in their eyes because they had done something that mattered. After this, they became a genuine part of our community. There is a big difference between *serving food to* the poor and *eating with* the poor. One says "you have deficits that I need to serve," the other says "you are a capable person, my friend."

Often, the best first step towards providing adequate health care for the poor isn't one directly related to providing medical care and technology, but one that gives attention to reversing socioeconomic conditions and environments that perpetuate the cycle of poverty and poor health. In the Dominican Republic, a 6,000-family village was transformed when the people participated in resolving issues in their poor community. First, they organized "the good faith cooperative store" that made nutritious food more accessible and reasonably priced. As the store succeeded and expanded, the people gained confidence and began to talk about developing better sources of safe drinking water and building a health clinic in the area (Outreach International 2005a).

In a number of poor subdivisions in South Texas, local residents found workable solutions to issues of public sanitation and safety, inadequate housing, and children's play areas (Outreach International 2005b). In Zambia, people took a genuine step out of poverty when supportive groups partnered with the people to create sustainable crops (Oxfam America 2005). A focus on building capacity has also enabled nurses in developed countries to create reciprocal partnerships with nurses in less developed countries, accomplishing significant goals that will benefit nurses and health care in both countries (CNA 2005; Ogilvie et al. 2003).

As these examples point out, the idea of

> A key to helping the poor, without crushing the spirit, is for us to acknowledge our mutual vulnerability.

helping people find their worthwhile place in the community works; it rebuilds lives and strengthens neighborhoods, villages, and nations. We have to wonder, then, why this isn't standard practice in our care for the poor.

Mutual Vulnerability

Too often, in the process of helping the poor, we crush their spirits by our approaches or attitudes. A key to helping the poor, without crushing the spirit, is for us to acknowledge our mutual vulnerability. Mutual vulnerability is a willingness on our part to recognize our own weaknesses and susceptibilities and to expose them to others in a caring manner that acknowledges common needs and shared struggles.

> *If an aim of nursing practice is compassionate engagement with patients, vulnerability cannot be conceptualized in terms of patient susceptibility alone, as though it were a risk factor that could or should be eliminated. Vulnerability is an ever-present aspect of being human, and recognition of mutual vulnerability is a way to preserve on a societal level the value of caring for others. (Malone 2000, 10)*

Revealing our own vulnerability sends a message that we are not immune to problems, that we share common human experiences. Use of our own vulnerability may seem unprofessional, but when used in a sincere and thoughtful manner, it can create empathy, initiate dialogue, and empower others. As professionals, we may bring and apply many valuable resources to the problems of the poor, but we can never know circumstances the way people in the midst of the problem do. When people realize a professional doesn't have all the answers it "empowers that person to use his or her own resources and insights to help themselves and others" (Mirow 2003).

Mutual vulnerability allows the poor to give to others—an act that gives them a dignity that can begin to transform their lives. Due to illness, I have been on the receiving end of care, concern, and empathy from both homeless women and refugee friends on at least two occasions. Though they had limited material possessions, these people were generous with comfort and offers to help me. My weakness broke down barriers and built relationships that would not have developed if I had remained only a strong, professional woman in their eyes. No one offered me more compassion than those who knew what it was like to feel utterly vulnerable. They understood better than most my frustration at not being able to work or to do certain things for myself. These unforgettable experiences taught me enormous lessons about the capacities of the poor and the beautiful gifts they have to offer.

Health care providers are automatically accorded positions of power over their patients because of their professional knowledge, competence, and status in society. This power position is often magnified for the poor, who have few resources and little status. Since circumstances generally lead refugees to view Americans as having positions of power over them, poor refugees are often in extremely powerless positions. These power differences affect authority, health-seeking behaviors, compliance, communication, and the development of relationships (Mirow 2003).

The power ascribed to professionals creates barriers or distance between health care workers and the poor. Awareness of the effects of power, however, enables nurses to find ways to close the distance and create effective relationships with those they desire to help.

Daniel suggests that nurses have the option between being in "power with" or in "power over" relationships (1998, 192). "Power with" relationships allow for partnerships that foster capabilities, while "power over" relationships permit us to commit "dehumanizing acts."

We must decide how we will use our power. Will we use it for our own gain and to improve our own status at the expense of others, or will we use it to show compassion, to stand against

> No one offered me more compassion than those who knew what it was like to feel utterly vulnerable.

exploitation of the poor, and to fight to give them a place in the community?

In some cases, the poor are poor because of bad choices regarding their lifestyles, relationships, or work habits—and they suffer because of this. But we must remember that the rich also make bad choices regarding their lifestyles, relationships, and business practices; however, wealth often allows them to cover over their mistakes and limit their exposure and suffering. The difference isn't in human nature as much as it is in resources and opportunities. At any level of society, at any time, we are vulnerable to harm and suffering, sometimes by our own hand, sometimes not.

Acknowledging our own vulnerability makes us more sensitive to the struggles of the poor and leads us to speak more kindly and to act more mercifully towards them. Awareness of our own weaknesses compels us to *walk with* the poor as they face the health care system, meet potential employers, seek solutions to their problems, and try to find their place in the community.

Listening To The Poor

Often, the most therapeutic thing we can do for the poor is to listen to them. Our presence and our unwearied listening—to their struggles, misfortunes, and their efforts to make changes—can provide more significant and compassionate care than any physical care we might offer. Active listening is a gesture that can help the poor feel human, respected, and genuinely cared for. We may not always find immediate solutions. The poor may leave our presence with the same troubles and problems with which they came, yet they can leave better off if they have received kindness, gentleness, and compassion from us.

> *Is there something I can do to be a voice for the poor? What can I do to give one person some dignity and self worth?*

Nurses who want to improve the health of the poor must look at more than physical symptoms, and listen to more than spoken words. We must listen with all of our senses as well as with our presence. We must *hear* the message hidden beneath the surface; and we must ask, "Is there something I can do to be a voice for the poor? What can I do to give one person some dignity and self worth?"

I have seen how such a simple act as active listening can make a difference in the health care of the poor.

At the beginning of the new millennium, the World Bank commenced a major study with the goal of greatly reducing the number of people living in extreme poverty by 2015. Their first step in this massive effort was to *listen to* "more than 60,000 poor women and men from 60 countries, in an unprecedented effort to understand poverty from the perspective of the poor themselves." The World Bank moved from this initial phase into numerous effective strategies for meaningful action; but the entire project began with the simple, yet profound, act of listening.

The World Bank's "participatory research" resulted in *Voices of the Poor*, a multifaceted work that "chronicles the struggles and aspirations of poor people for a life of dignity." As a result of this listening, the researchers heard this from the poor across five continents: "Poverty is voiceless. It's powerlessness. It's insecurity and humiliation." They concluded, "If we are to succeed in this task, we must include, involve and *listen* to poor people and their representatives" (Dodd & Munck 2002, 2; The World Bank Group, "What is *Voices of the Poor?*"n.d., ¶ 2). What they heard should be our wake-up call to do just that—

> Ludka's[2] baby daughter was failing to thrive, and ended up in the hospital. As a recent refugee, she was dependent on public assistance, and most of the professionals who tried to help her were rushed and impatient. Because of her limited use of the English language, they viewed Ludka as incompetent and tended to blame her for the baby's problems. However, as I visited in her apartment, I could see that she had attempted many appropriate interventions to help her child. I "listened" as she showed me what she had tried, demonstrated the baby's behavior, walked me through her routines, and even opened her refrigerator to display its healthy contents. Though I knew only a few words from her language, I sensed the shame and frustration she was experiencing over her daughter's inability to eat and grow; and saw the tremendous relief on her face after I assured her that she was a good mother and was doing all she could for her daughter. On her next visit to the hospital, we were able to secure an appropriate translator and communicate her situation more accurately, with the result that the health care team found a workable and successful intervention. For many weeks afterwards, she proudly announced her daughter's ever-increasing weight each time I returned to visit.
>
> 2. Name has been changed

include, involve, and listen to the poor, so we can help relieve their hopelessness.

Jesus Made A Place For The Poor

Jesus offers a model of care for those who desire to help the poor feel like whole human beings. Jesus was passionate in his concern for the poor, welcomed them, and made a place for them in the community. Though their society rejected and often blamed them for their problems, he showed his love for them by walking, talking, and eating with them. His attitude towards the poor often confused the important church leaders of his day, but it attracted the lowly.

Jesus once shocked a crowd of listeners by telling them that they should invite the poor to their banquets, instead of the prominent or the rich (Luke 14:12-14; Luke 15:1-2). He compassionately preserved the dignity of the poor, instructing his disciples to be so quiet and secretive when giving to the poor that their left hand would not even know what their right hand was doing (Matthew 6:2-4). When he saw that the money changers had made a market out of the one portion of the temple designated for the poor and the foreigners, he became angry, flipped over their loaded tables, and forced them to leave (Mark 11:15-17).

Jesus identified with the poor. He willingly was born into poverty, lived as a refugee (Matthew 2:13), and was homeless all of his adult life (Matthew 8:20). He showed particular concern for poor, broken, and dejected people from the very beginning of his ministry, when he proclaimed that God had sent him "to preach good news to the poor…to proclaim freedom for the prisoners and recovery of sight for the blind, to release the oppressed" (Luke 4:18-19 NIV). He offered those in need a great gift of hope.

Jesus turned the world's values complete-

ly upside down when he honored a poor widow who had only two small coins to place in the offering basket at the temple in Jerusalem. While others most likely scoffed at her lowly, meager gift, Jesus affirmed and dignified her by saying, "this poor widow has put in more than all the others. All these people gave their gifts out of their wealth; but she out of her poverty put in all she had to live on" (Luke 21:1-4 NIV). The rich, who put larger amounts into the temple treasury that day, have long been forgotten; but the widow and her greater gift have reminded and instructed people for centuries of the true spirit of giving.

Jesus was aware that lowly, weak, and poor people often made mistakes which caused them to suffer, but he still welcomed them, enjoyed fellowship with them, and was willing to use them in his mission; in fact, it was their awareness of their great need that enabled them to receive redemption and find purpose (Luke 5:29-32). Once after Jesus had healed a naked, insane, and seemingly useless man, he immediately sent him out to share a witness of God's amazing healing and mercy (Mark 5:1-20). Another time, Jesus talked with and listened to an outcast woman, then used her to share his grace with her whole village (John 4).

> *It is only through awareness of his or her own great need that anyone receives redemption and finds a purpose, or a place, in the community.*

In his compassion for the poor, Jesus did not spurn the rich. Instead, he emphasized that both rich and poor alike need community:

> *When Jesus asked the rich young man to sell his good and give to the poor, he did not say "Become destitute and friendless." Rather, he said, "Come, follow me" (Mt. 19:21). In other words, he invited him to join a community of sharing and love, where his security would not be based on individual*

property holdings, but on openness to the Spirit and on the loving care of new-found brothers and sisters. (Taylor 1973, 21)

After an encounter with Jesus, Zacchaeus, a wealthy, dishonest tax collector, discovered that he wanted fellowship with Jesus and with his neighbors more than he wanted wealth. As a result, he ended up giving half of his possessions to the poor, and promised to repay four times the amount he had taken from those he had cheated (Luke 19:1-10). The story of Zacchaeus illustrates the fact that, just like the poor, the rich often make mistakes that cause them to suffer.

> *Nurses and other health care workers have the opportunity to help the poor transform their lives...*

True, inclusive community, as Jesus taught it, can bring blessings to both the poor and the non-poor alike. Through mutual vulnerability in community we come to "realize that weaknesses can turn out to be strengths," and make us "more apt to depend on God and less inclined to be judgmental of others" (Paige 1999, 9). One may share from his or her rich resources and material possessions, another may give great gifts from a humble spirit; in the process, both will likely learn the value of sharing their gifts with one another and come to discover that it is only through awareness of his or her own great need that anyone receives redemption and finds a purpose, or a place, in the community.

Conclusion

Around the world, poverty depletes people's health and hope. Poor people often become dispirited because they feel worthless, powerless, and vulnerable. Nurses and other health care workers have the opportunity to help the poor transform their lives and communities by finding their gifts, contributions, and abilities and seeking ways to involve the poor in unique solutions to their own problems. This should be our standard practice. By viewing the poor as Jesus did, we can help them find a welcome and meaningful place in our communities.

NOTES

1   Name has been changed.

QUESTIONS FOR DISCUSSION

1. The author believes that the poor are often defined in light of their problems, rather than in terms of their abilities. Why do you think society approaches them in this way?

2. "One of the most important keys to successful transformation in the lives of the poor is the incorporation of the poor into the process of transformation." What does this statement mean to you? How might you apply it in your practice?

3. The author points out that there is a difference between serving food to the poor and eating with the poor. In what ways are these activities different? Discuss this difference with members of your group.

4. The author believes that health care providers can support the poor by being open about their own vulnerability and need for support. She notes that, "Revealing our own vulnerability sends a message that we are not immune to problems, that we share common human experiences." Do you feel comfortable showing your vulnerability to those to whom you give care? Why or why not?

5. What do the poor gain when they are listened to by others? Why do those who listen to them gain from the process?

6. Describe the attitude of Jesus toward the poor. What did he do in his lifetime to promote their interests?

7. What actions might you take to help the poor in your community? Outline three possibilities and share them with your group.

SCENARIOS FOR LEARNING AND GROWTH

Read through the following scenarios and discuss the questions that follow them with the members of your group.

SCENARIO ONE

You are working in the office of a primary care physician near a lower middle-class neighborhood. You are preparing a young woman, Mrs. Green, for a prenatal exam by the physician. Mrs. Green has two small children in the room with her—a typical situation for most of the young female clients from the nearby neighborhood. While you are asking questions and making notes in the chart, you notice the young woman is fighting back tears. When you ask her about it, she hesitates, and then tells you that her husband was just sent to jail for a year. Without his job she no longer has health care insurance. She is afraid she can't return for any more visits and doesn't know how she will pay for the birth of the baby. Mrs. Green has some skills and wants to work, but doesn't know who will hire her since she is pregnant. Also, she has no idea what she would do to provide child care for her other children.

1. *Define the problem presented in this scenario.*

2. *What options are available to those involved?*

3. *What actions might be taken to prevent a similar situation from occurring in the future?*

4. *How could you help this client find a place in the community?*

5. *What have you learned from this scenario and how might you apply it to your work?*

SCENARIO TWO

You are a nurse working in the emergency room. One of your patients is Mrs. White, a 50-year-old woman who came in with severe abdominal pain. After doing an initial assessment on her, you notice that the emergency room physician has not ordered all of the usual tests for Mrs. White. You give her the ordered pain medication, and see that the ordered tests are carried out. Mrs. White has a mild fever, and continues to have pain and nausea. You report this to the physician, who is slow to respond and takes care of a less acute patient first. While you wait at the central desk area, you overhear the physician explaining to a physician's assistant that a minimum of tests and the least expensive medications have been ordered for Mrs. White because she has no insurance or means to pay for her care. The physician is very abrupt when assessing Mrs. White, and brushes off her husband's questions.

Mrs. White's husband is quite anxious about her care. He pulls you aside and tells you it was hard to get her to even come to the hospital, because she was so worried about the bills and embarrassed that they didn't have a way to pay them. Mr. White holds his head down and avoids looking you in the eye as he confesses to you that he feels badly about not having any insurance. He explains that he was laid off a year ago, and says, "It isn't easy for a man my age to find work. I have been looking and looking." He adds, "Please take good care of my wife. I will find a way to pay the bill, whatever it is."

After Mrs. White's test results come back, the physician orders an antibiotic and some pain pills, and discharges her from the hospital. Her husband is still quite worried and says to you, "Do you think it is okay for her to go home? Don't you think she should be admitted to the hospital?"

You find the physician and question the discharge order, but are told, "She will be fine at home. The antibiotics and the pain pills will help." You delay a little longer with her care, hoping to find some reason to keep Mrs. White in the hospital, but finally, reluctantly, you discharge her.

You find out later that she returned to the hospital in worse condition and was admitted. She ended up having acute abdominal surgery and nearly died.

1. Describe the problem presented in this scenario.

2. What options are available to those involved?

3. What actions might be taken to prevent a similar situation from occurring in the future?

4. How could you help these clients find a place in the community?

5. What have you learned from this scenario and how might you apply it to your work?

SCENARIO THREE

You have been in a remote area of a developing country for two weeks as a volunteer with a medical team that has been providing health care clinics and minor surgeries. You raised your own money for this trip, and worked hard with your team to collect supplies and equipment to bring along for the clinics you have been holding. Your family and friends all gathered with you for a big send-off at the airport. This trip is something you have dreamed of doing all your life and you are excited to be here to serve the poor people of this region.

With the help of your translator, you have been trying to do a lot of health teaching, along with the physical care. You feel good that you have been able to share important information with the people regarding matters of health, such as infant care and basic hygiene.

Your patients have been extremely grateful to receive the care you are providing, and quite a number of the people have brought you food and gifts, which you have quickly set aside, because you don't want them to think this is why you are here. Many of the people have offered to help your team with the work, to clean the area, carry supplies, and do whatever they can to help. But, in order to keep things efficient, you have declined most of their help. Besides, you want them to know they are special, that you care about them, and want to serve them.

You regret that you have only had a little time to spend in the village itself, getting to know the people, but your team has not wanted to waste time doing that when there is so much work to be done. However, you have been taking lots of pictures of the people and the clinics, and can't wait to show the folks back home how, with their support, you were able to provide so much help and make such a difference in the lives of these desperately poor people who live in such humble and deprived conditions.

1. Describe the problem in this scenario.

2. What options are available to those involved?

3. What actions might be taken to prevent a similar situation from occurring in the future?

4. How might you help the people in this scenario find a place in the community?

5. What have you learned from this scenario and how might you apply it in your work?

REFERENCES

Canadian Nurses Association (CNA). 2005. International health partnerships. http://cna-aiic.ca/CNA/international/partnerships/default_e.aspx.

Daniel, L. 1998. Vulnerability as a key to authenticity. *Image: Journal of Nursing Scholarship* 30 (2): 191-192.

Davis, B. 1990. Don't Throw Bread From The Truck. *World Vision Magazine* Aug-Sept. http://www.globalcompassion.com/article.htm.

Dodd, R., and L. Munck, eds. 2002. Dying for change: Poor people's experience of health and ill-health. http://www1.worldbank.org/prem/poverty/voices/reports/dying/index.htm.

International Council of Nurses (ICN). n.d. ICN on poverty and health: Breaking the link. ICN website at http://www.icn.ch/matters_poverty.htm.

Malone, R. E. 2000. Dimensions of vulnerability in emergency nurses' narratives. *Advances in Nursing Science* 23 (1): 1-11.

McKnight, J. 1995. Why "servanthood" is bad. *The Other Side* Nov-Dec: 56-59.

Mirow, R. 2003. The power of vulnerability. *Learning disability practice* 6 (10): 36-39.

Ogilvie, L., M. Allen, J. Laryea, and M. Opare. 2003. Building capacity through a collaborative international nursing project. *Journal of Nursing Scholarship* 35 (2): 113-118.

Outreach International. 2005a. The good faith cooperative store. http://www.outreach-international.org/page/183.

———. 2005b. USA-Texas. http://www.outreach-international.org/page/58.

———. 2005c. Who we are. http://www.outreach-international.org/page/who/.

Oxfam America. 2005. Zambia: Taking steps toward food security. http://www.oxfamamerica.org/whatwedo/where_we_work/southern_africa/news_publications/art5773.html/?searchterm=zambia.

Paige, R. 1999. Renewed to walk with the poor. *Journal of Christian Nursing* 16 (1): 7-11.

Rogers, A. C. 1997. Vulnerability, health and health care. *Journal of Advanced Nursing* 26:65-72.

Taylor, R. 1973. *Economics and the gospel: A primer on shalom as economic justice.* Philadelphia: United Church Press.

The World Bank Group. n.d. From Voices to Action. http://www1.worldbank.org/prem/poverty/voices/vtoa.htm.

The World Bank Group. n.d. What is *Voices of the Poor?* http://www1.worldbank.org/prem/poverty/voices/overview.htm.

Some helpful websites on Poverty, Health, and Empowerment of the Poor

International Council of Nurses: http://www.icn.ch/

Mennonite Central Committee: http://www.mennonitecc.ca/

Outreach International: http://www.outreach-international.org/

Oxfam America: http://www.oxfamamerica.org

The World Bank Group: http://www.worldbank.org/

World Health Organization: http://www.who.int/en/

Just Generosity: A New Vision For Overcoming Poverty In America

by Ronald J. Sider

Summary: Neither the government nor faith-based organizations alone can provide the reformation needed to overcome poverty in America. Sider provides a clear picture of poverty in America, describes the new vision that is necessary to change the future of the poor in this country, and calls on the Christian community to respond with justice.

We could end the scandal of widespread poverty in the richest nation in history. We could seize one of the most significant opportunities in a century for Christians to transform society. The key to this transformation will be a new holistic vision that awakens Christians to their call to seek justice for the poor in public arenas, expands the role of religious faith in meeting the real needs of the poor, and shows how families, churches, businesses, the media, schools, and government can all work together to play their proper role. What we need is a new holistic vision.

According to the U.S. Bureau of the Census, about 36 million Americans live at the poverty level or below. That is the highest poverty rate of all industrialized nations. The welfare rolls have dropped dramatically (46 percent since 1994), but the poverty level remains stubbornly high.

What would it be like to live in the United States on $19,350 a year? Try to imagine what your family, or the family of four you know best, would need to give up to exist on $19,350 a year. Begin by selling your house and moving to a modest two-bedroom apartment ($711 a month including heat). No more study, recreation room, bedroom for each child, second bathroom, backyard, or porch. If you are willing to live in a lower-income, multiracial neighborhood, you might be able to buy a small house.

Next, sell all your cars. You don't have a garage anyway. You can get around on public transportation, or perhaps you can afford an old car—only $49 a week for transportation.

> We could end the scandal of widespread poverty in the richest nation in history.

Forget about being in fashion. New clothes each season are unthinkable. If you visit the local thrift store for most things, you can probably get by on $359 per person per year.

You will no longer be able to afford to

Ronald J. Sider, Ph.D., is Professor of Theology, Holistic Ministry and Public Policy and Director of the Sider Center on Ministry and Public Policy at Eastern Baptist Theological Seminary. He is also President of Evangelicals for Social Action and has spoken on six continents, published twenty-seven books and scores of articles. His book Rich Christians in an Age of Hunger was recognized by Christianity Today as one of the one hundred most influential religious books of the twentieth century.

This essay is a summary of key ideas from Ronald J. Sider. 1999. *Just Generosity: A New Vision for Overcoming Poverty in America*. Grand Rapids: Baker.

eat at restaurants. You will have to figure out how to avoid hunger and stay healthy on just a little more than $1 per meal for each person.

No more regular telephone calls to Grandma, other relatives, or friends in other cities. Your telephone budget is just $32 a month, which leaves you out of having a cell phone or an Internet connection. And be sure to turn off the lights when you leave a room because you have only $48 a month for all utilities not included in your rent.

Let's look at the totals.

What is the total? $19,348. The 2005 poverty level was $19,350, so you have two dollars for a call to Grandma once a year on

Table 1	
Living at the Poverty Level (Family of Four)	
housing	8,532
utilities	972
food	4,380
transportation	2,548
clothing	1,436
Social Security taxes	1,480
	(for a full-time worker earning minimum wage)
	19,348

her birthday.

This budget does not include any money for "luxuries" like visits to a doctor or dentist, household appliances, vacations, sports, church, or Christmas gifts. Obviously, poor people do have some of those things. Somehow, they manage to spend even less on the basics I outlined.

Any volunteers? What do you suppose the God of justice thinks about that kind of widespread poverty in the richest nation on earth?

U.S. society is becoming more and more unequal. In 1974, the richest fifth enjoyed seven times as much income as the poorest fifth. Twenty years later, when the poor were worse off, the rich had *eleven* times as much!

If we compare wealth rather than income, the inequality is even more marked—and getting worse. In 1998, the richest 20 percent had 85 percent of all the wealth in the U.S. In fact, the richest *one* percent owned more wealth than all the rest of us in the bottom *95 percent*. The U.S. has the most unequal distribution of wealth of all industrialized nations.

While CEO salaries have escalated, the working poor have lost ground. In 1965, the average CEO made about 44 times the salary of the average factory worker. Thirty years later, it was 209 times and growing. If the average factory worker had received pay raises comparable to CEOs in the years 1980-1995, they would have earned $90,000 by 1995 and the minimum-wage worker would have enjoyed $39,000 a year instead of less than $10,000. In reality, the minimum wage is worth less after inflation than 30 years ago.

What should we do? Is there any comprehensive strategy that could dramatically reduce poverty in the U.S.?

A New Vision

We need to evaluate the basic strategies of the last four decades using both biblical norms and factual data in order to develop a new vision and approach. The fundamental biblical norms for this evaluation are clear. God created persons as body-soul beings made for community. Made in the divine image, we are to be co-workers with the Creator, creating wealth, promoting the common good and caring for our neighbors. Work is our joy and responsibility. God wants every person and family to have access to the productive resources they need in order to earn their own way and be dignified members of their community. (As a friend of mine says, "Private property is so good, everybody ought to have some.") Because sinful people with power regularly oppress the weak and poor, the God who loves everyone equally actively sides with the poor, demanding that his people correct unfair social systems so that everyone enjoys genuine opportunity for a decent life.

How well have our policies in the last four decades measured up to this standard? In 1962, Michael Harrington published a now-famous book called *The Other America*, which significantly influenced the Kennedy-Johnson War on Poverty. Rejecting private charitable approaches as unworkable, Harrington, like other liberals, placed all his hope in better government programs. For a decade or two, the brightest and best liberal thinkers in Washington and the universities believed the right government policies could end poverty.

Did it work? Not really. Of course, some programs worked quite well. The sweeping claim that all government programs have failed is simply false. In 2001, only one in ten elderly Americans were poor. Why? Because of a government program called Social Security. Without that, about 50 percent of all our elderly folk would have been poor in 2001. A number of government programs have worked quite well.

One stubborn fact, however, remains. The poverty level has remained high. The terrible poverty in our inner cities has grown worse.

Biblical faith helps us understand what went wrong. Secular liberals thought they could end poverty merely by governmental modification of the external environment. But biblical people know that persons are not just material beings responding to economic incentives. We are also spiritual beings who make wrong choices. From a biblical perspective, any approach to ending poverty that neglects personal moral and spiritual causes and solutions is bound to fail.

By the early eighties, the liberal dream of ending poverty had collapsed. In fact, conservative analyst Charles Murray argued in *Losing Ground* (1984) that the big government programs had made things worse. According to Murray, welfare grants, food stamps, etc., had undermined the family and destroyed responsibility and work. His solution? Different *government* policies! Just abolish welfare payments, etc., and force the poor to work. And conservatives did cut some government programs for the poor, although they never enacted Murray's drastic proposals. What happened? The number of people in poverty remained high in spite of a growing economy.

In 1992, evangelical journalist Marvin Olasky suggested a new approach. He argued in *The Tragedy of American Compassion* that we ought to substitute private, charitable faith-based programs for government anti-poverty measures. That suggestion was half-right; the partial truth is crucially important.

Persons are body-soul beings, so if we work only at the material, economic side, we are dealing with only half of the problem and get, at best, only half a solution. Olasky is right that we need a greatly expanded emphasis on the role of faith-based agencies in overcoming poverty. The tragedy of Olasky's book is that he neglects the structural causes of poverty, emphasizing only the moral and spiritual causes and solutions. In his view, government has, at best, a very small role to

> From a biblical perspective, any approach to ending poverty that neglects personal moral and spiritual causes and solutions is bound to fail.

play in combating poverty. That is as one-sided and unbiblical as the earlier secular liberalism of Michael Harrington.

Biblical faith and careful analysis of recent social history suggest that we need a comprehensive, integrated vision that understands that poverty in the U.S. results both from wrong personal choices about things like drugs, sex, marriage, and work and also from economic structures that are unfair.

One recent study tried to determine the relative importance of these two different factors in the ongoing persistence of U.S. poverty: Is it due primarily to economic factors like falling wages for low-skilled workers or primarily due to the drastic decline in two-parent families? Their findings? Both—in roughly equal proportions! That means that we can end poverty neither by simply creating better economic arrangements nor by merely renewing stable two-parent families. We need both.

> The Bible knows that both personal spiritual renewal and genuine economic opportunity are necessary.

Biblical people are not surprised. The Bible talks about both personal and social sin. The Bible knows that both personal spiritual renewal and genuine economic opportunity are necessary. People need Jesus and jobs.

A Balanced Biblical Perspective

A balanced biblical perspective also helps us answer the hotly debated question: How much should government do to overcome poverty? Many secular liberals wanted government to do almost everything. Libertarians (including a number of conservative Christians) want it to do almost nothing.

At many points in the Bible, we see that the first responsibility to help needy persons rests with the family. In Leviticus 25, the next of kin in the extended family is the first place to look for help (vv. 25, 35; cf. also 1 Tim. 5:16). The New Testament repeatedly places great emphasis on the church's responsibility to care for the poor (Acts 2, 4). Family, church, and neighbors ought to be the first to assist needy persons.

But the Bible also clearly teaches that government has a role. In the Jubilee text, if no family member is there to help, the poor person has a legal right to get his land back at the next Jubilee (Lev. 25:28). The Old Testament repeatedly talks about the responsibility of the king to help the poor: "The Lord … has made you king to execute justice and righteousness" (1 Kings 10:9 NRSV; cf. Jer. 22:15-16). Careful study of these two words — *justice* and *righteousness* — shows that they refer to both fair legal systems and just economic structures. Psalm 72 (one of the royal Psalms that discuss the role of the king) declares, "May he defend the cause of the poor of the people, give deliverance to the needy; and crush the oppressor" (v. 4 NRSV). The oppressor who needs to be crushed in this text is not some totalitarian governmental structure but rather oppressive people whom the state needs to restrain in order to bring justice to the poor.

Simple arithmetic also demonstrates that private charity cannot do it all. There are about 325,000 religious congregations (churches, synagogues, etc.) in the U.S. If they took over just four basic government anti-poverty programs (welfare, food stamps, SSI, and EITC), each congregation would have to find another $289,000 per year. If they also took over just the federal government's share of medical care (Medicaid) for the poor, the annual figure would be $612,000 per congregation. That would be rather difficult since the present total median annual budget per congregation is only $50,000-$60,000! Government does play a crucial role. But it is not the only role, and often not even the primary role.

One of the most important public policy developments in years is the stunning new openness to the role that religious faith and religious agencies must play if we are to overcome poverty. In 1993 in *The Culture of Disbelief*, Yale law professor Stephen Carter accurately described (and lamented) the way that religious faith was dismissed or marginalized in elite circles including government. By 1998, Rev. Eugene Rivers was on the cover of *Newsweek* in a story exploring the possibility that churches might be able to succeed in the battle against urban poverty and violence when every other tactic had failed. Increasing evidence showing that faith-based groups like Teen Challenge are far more successful than secular programs is convincing public policy experts to welcome a much-expanded role for religious service providers. Government now eagerly welcomes people of faith to play a significantly expanded role, especially in combating poverty. Christians today face an historic opportunity that we have not enjoyed in decades.

A new holistic vision includes embracing this expanded role for religious faith in the fight against poverty. This significantly expanded role for civil society (family, church, etc.) is crucial because faith-based social service agencies can deal with the whole person, combining spiritual renewal and material aid, in a way that government agencies simply cannot and should not. Fortunately, the Charitable Choice provision in the 1996 federal welfare reform legislation opened the door to a much-needed expansion of faith-based programs in the battle against poverty. If we can do that and at the same time insist that business, the media, unions, and government also do their proper part, we could dramatically reduce poverty in this nation in the next two decades.

I want to examine five critical areas, applying this holistic strategy. A comprehensive agenda for overcoming poverty will have many parts, but these five are especially crucial: a living wage for all who work; renewed two-parent families; health care for everyone; schools that work for everyone, especially the poor and minorities; and justice and faith in action through churches.

Living Wage

People who are able to work have an obligation to do so. When they do that responsibly, they should not be poor. Tragically, millions of our neighbors today in this rich nation work full time all year round yet remain mired in poverty. Over one-third of all poor children in our country live in a family where at least one parent is working full time. Forty percent of all black and Latino single moms work full time without escaping poverty. The same is true for 22 percent of all black men. Even at the peak of our booming economy, five million workers in the U.S. wanted full time work but could only find part-time employment.

We should decide as a society that everyone who can work should work, that all who want to work will have a full-time job, and that any family in which parents collectively work at least 40 hours a week will receive after-tax compensation equal to 120-130 percent of the national poverty level. In order to reach that goal, five things are important:

1. Expand the refundable Earned Income Tax Credit (EITC). Currently, if a person with children works at low wages, they receive a federal tax credit for every dollar they earn up to a certain level. Especially important is the provision that if their income is so low that they do not owe any taxes, they still get the money from the government (that is what the word *refundable* means). The EITC rewards work and strengthens the family. We should expand it.

2. Strengthen the food stamp program. We must insist that all legal immigrants are

> We should decide as a society that everyone who can work should work and that all who want to work will have a full-time job.

eligible for food stamps and assist those who are eligible in applying. Recently, states have been given more options as to how they may value a family's care when determining eligibility for food stamps. We should make sure that all states allow working families to own a reliable means of transportation without jeopardizing their ability to receive food stamps.

3. Raise the minimum wage a little. I am glad to let economists decide on the most effective mix of EITC, food stamps, and minimum wage. Most economists today, however, believe that a modest increase in the minimum wage would help the poor. It is currently $5.15 per hour. Even if we raised it to $5.50 it would still be lower (when adjusted for inflation) than 30 years ago.

> *Unless our preachers and prophets renew people of moral integrity who keep their promises to their children and spouses, all other efforts will fail.*

4. Change and expand the Dependent Care Tax Credit. Workers with dependents currently may receive a tax credit for part of the cost of their childcare. But it is not refundable, so poor families (who owe no federal taxes) do not receive a cent. Only middle-class families benefit. This tax credit should be refundable. Further, two-parent families where parents collectively work at least 40 hours a week should be eligible. Currently only two-parent families where both parents work outside the home are eligible. The result? Families that treasure parenting so much that one parent stays at home with young children subsidize the childcare for families where both parents work! Every pro-family group ought to endorse an expanded, refundable dependent care tax credit.

5. Guarantee a job for everyone able and willing to work. At any given time, millions of people in the U.S. who are looking for a job are not likely to find one. Refugees who are legally welcomed into this country often find it difficult to find appropriate work before they reach the end of their temporary assistance. It is a violation of biblical justice for a wealthy society to fail to offer a job to everyone willing and able to work. We should promote job development in our communities, with government as an employer of last resort to guarantee a job to all who cannot find regular employment by another means.

Renewing Two-Parent Families

Princeton sociologist Sara McLanahan, an investigator for The Fragile Families and Child Wellbeing Study, puts it bluntly: "The more single parents, the more poverty." In the U.S., children in one-parent families are 11 times more likely to experience persistent poverty than children in two-parent families. U.S. Census data consistently shows that the poverty rate for single-parent families is much higher than that for two-parent families. Unfortunately, the U.S. has the highest divorce rate and one of the highest out-of-wedlock birth rates. Single parenthood resulting from divorce and out-of-wedlock births is one of the most important economic justice issues of our time.

What can be done? Clearly, the causes of single parenthood are complex. We might blame businesses that maximize profits, and corporations that pressure their managers for even greater productivity with little regard for the way long hours undermine family life. There are undoubtedly government policies that are far from family-friendly. But it would be silly to think that these are the primary place to solve this problem. The primary responsibility for renewing stable, wholesome two-parent families lies with the church!

Eighty-four percent of the people in this society claim to be Christian. We need massively expanded programs in the churches to persuade Moms and Dads to keep their marriage vows. Unless our preachers and prophets renew people of moral integrity who keep their promises to their children and spouses, all other efforts will fail.

The media could make a major contribution if they would drastically reduce the amount of sex and violence they disseminate. Businesses could voluntarily expand the opportunities for flexible working arrangements so that parents can more easily meet family responsibilities. Government could make it easier for poor families to own their own homes through tax credits. A living wage, universal health insurance, and quality education for all would also reduce the pressure that weakens families. We need all of the above and more if we are to correct the decay in our families that contributes so much to poverty. Our only hope is a holistic, comprehensive approach that begins with a strong role for the church and people of faith.

Health Insurance for Everyone

Over 45 million Americans (or 15.6 percent of the population) lack health insurance; the lower the income, the less likely a family has health insurance. Half of all poor people who work full time are uninsured. Tragically, the number of uninsured goes up year after year.

Studies show that the uninsured are four times more likely to report that they needed medical care but did not get it. When they do see a doctor, they receive inferior medical care. The result? Three and one half million people go to the hospital every year without insurance and the billions of unpaid bills that result exact heavy financial and emotional burdens. The poor have more illness than the non-poor do. They also die younger.

We must tell our legislators that 45 million uninsured Americans is a moral outrage that we refuse to accept. I wish every congregation would initiate a simple letter-writing campaign that demands that within four years they have in place some workable scheme that guarantees health insurance to every person in this wealthy land. How can pro-family Christian political voices not demand health insurance for poor families?

Quality Education for All, Even the Poor

Our schools are simply not working for millions of poor Americans. Jesse Jackson is right: One child is programmed for Yale, another for jail.

We live in an information society where knowledge is the most important capital. Poorly educated people are seriously disadvantaged. Minorities and the urban poor are the most likely to receive a poor education or to drop out of school. Inferior education is one of the primary causes of economic injustice today. Interestingly, studies show that poor schools have a greater negative impact on disadvantaged children than on others, but good schools have a stronger positive impact on disadvantaged children than on others. Quality education is the best way to empower the poorest children. Educational opportunity is the new civil rights struggle.

The causes of the inferior education received by poor and minority children are many and complex — lingering racism, unsafe, drug-infested neighborhoods, dysfunctional families, malnutrition, oversized administrative bureaucracies, unresponsive teachers' unions, and peer pressure that mocks academic success. There is no quick fix to that long litany of problems.

Increasing numbers of people, however,

> ...poor schools have a greater negative impact on disadvantaged children than on others, but good schools have a stronger positive impact on disadvantaged children than on others.

think that educational vouchers, at least to lower-income families, would help significantly. Others strongly prefer reforming the public schools — smaller classes, better qualified teachers, more equitable funding, more emphases on the basics, stricter graduation standards. The list of good reforms is lengthy. I do believe the time is ripe for a major test. Why not a five-year test in which we spend roughly equal money on two parallel tests: a) a major test of vouchers in a dozen places; b) a test of the best "reform the public schools" proposals in a dozen places. Especially important for everyone concerned with justice will be the

> *Just a few years ago, Leslie Brown was a single mom with three children and a live-in boyfriend. She barely scraped by on welfare and public housing. Fortunately, Leslie heard the gospel and became an active Christian. Her boyfriend, Tony, also started attending church and soon became a Christian. Spiritual transformation, however, did not improve their awful financial situation.*
>
> *Joining Jobs Partnership made the difference.*
>
> *Two churches surrounded Leslie and Tony as they started the classes. Even before Tony completed the training, he found a job at a Pepsi company. Leslie also found part-time work. Tony and Leslie have been off welfare and out of public housing for over two years and are now married. Promoted four times, Tony is a foreman.*

impact on poor and minority children. If a careful test demonstrates that vouchers help them, widespread adoption would be warranted. If they hurt them, I will help lead the battle against vouchers.

For millions of poor children, effective educational reform is a matter of despair or hope. For far too many, it is literally an issue of life or death.

Justice and Faith in Action

Many of the above six measures are public policy initiatives, but that does not mean that other sectors of society have no responsibility. Business leaders should not wait for government to pay a living wage or create job-training programs for the least advantaged. Faith-based agencies like Jobs Partnership can offer job training that nurtures both spiritual and moral renewal and expanded technical skills.

Jobs Partnership began in 1996, when a Christian businessman, Chris Mangum, met inner-city pastor Rev. Donald McCoy. The businessman needed workers and the pastor needed jobs. Together they launched what has quickly become a highly successful job-training program that combines technical skill training, biblical values, and Christian mentors. A local church sponsors each student in Jobs Partnership. Through a personal mentor assigned by the church, the congregation provides transportation, childcare, even housing—and more important, love, encouragement, affirmation, and accountability. Church members walk with the participants for up to two years as they complete training and begin a job.

Lawndale Community Church (LCC) in Chicago shows how it works. Thirty years ago, the Lawndale community was discouraged and broken. In fact, it was one of the poorest 20 communities in the United States. Virtually nobody went to college from Lawndale's awful schools. The infant mortality rate approached third-world levels.

Over the past 20 years, however, Lawndale Community Church's social ministries have grown into a $13-million-a-year holistic program. They have built or remodeled millions of dollars of low-income housing. The health clinic has 22 full-time doctors. The college prep program has assisted and enabled 100 Lawndale youth to graduate from college. Fifty of them have returned to inner-city Lawndale to offer the same hope to their younger siblings and friends that LCC gave to them.

The health clinic is so successful (even though the doctors receive only one-third of a typical doctor's salary) that the infant mortality rate has dropped by 60 percent, making headlines in Chicago newspapers. The federal health officials in the Chicago region came to LCC to ask if they could fund some of LCC's enormously successful programs. Now the federal office requires its entire regional staff to read Wayne Gordon's book (*Real Hope in Chicago*) about LCC's amazing success.

Why is LCC so successful? There are many reasons: outstanding leadership, good funding, and help from the Chicago Bears. According to Wayne Gordon, however, the single most important reason for their success is faith. "None of this would work the way it does," Wayne says, "apart from the vibrant faith in Christ that motivates all our staff and the active relational evangelism that has led hundreds and hundreds of Lawndale residents to personal faith and transformed lives."

LCC staff do not cram religion down people's throats. But sensitively, carefully, the staff openly talk about the way faith in Christ transforms broken lives.

Good Samaritan Ministries (GSM), a faith-based agency working in partnership with state government (Michigan) to move welfare recipients to a job and self-sufficiency, is another example of how the Christian community can bring real hope to the poor.

Good Samaritan Ministries does not try to be either the government welfare agency or the local church. Rather, it is the bridge between them. Government contracts provide about one quarter of GSM's budget; the rest comes from private donations. The government administers the welfare programs, interviews applicants, and refers them to GSM's Relational Ministries. GSM links the welfare family to a congregation-based Relational Ministry Team which has been carefully trained by GSM in "transformational relationships," which includes a mixture of love, regular contact, emotional support, prayer, and individualized care that government agencies cannot provide. During training, they warn church volunteers: "You must be ready to change as much as you expect these families to change."

The ministry team establishes a close friendship with the welfare family, providing physical, social, emotional, and spiritual support for up to a year. The team is careful not to make the family dependent on them, but they offer whatever assistance is needed — help in finding an apartment, untangling legal problems, fixing or finding a car, emergency food and clothing, finding a job, improving work skills, and financial planning. Most important, however, they provide friendship. The church team is careful

> "You must be ready to change as much as you expect these families to change."

not to impose their beliefs, but they pray regularly for their new friends, and after earning the right by gentle caring, they freely share their faith and talk about the way that God can transform a person's values, character, and life. It works! Ottawa County, Michigan became the first county in America to put every able-bodied welfare recipient in a job. Mentoring programs similar to those in GSM are springing up in many places.

Real Hope for the Poor?

I have sketched a comprehensive holistic framework in which all the different institutions in society — family, church, media, unions, business, and government — each do what they do best. But I believe that if there is any realistic hope that our society

> *The story of Michele underlines the importance of the faith factor. Michele was frightened and alone. She was finishing a job-training program and hoping to leave welfare soon, but she had just three more weeks before she had to leave the transitional housing program where she and her one-year-old son lived. Fortunately, she discovered Bridge of Hope, a church-based mentoring program for homeless mothers.*
>
> *A team from Hinkletown Mennonite Church near Lancaster, Pennsylvania, helped her find an apartment, a day care center, and a car. They even took turns driving her to work until Michele was able to renew her expired driver's license. Michele credits her mentoring team for her improved parenting skills and encouraging her dream of owning her own home, which she recently purchased. Most important, though, they led her to personal faith. "My mentors have helped me grow spiritually simply by the way they loved me through Jesus," Michele says. "I have learned to trust in him because he is the only one who truly knows what is best for me. This is the one thing that has helped me succeed."*
>
> *Bridge of Hope has helped over 75 homeless women like Michele. They now have materials available for church groups who want to establish an affiliate in their own community.*

will implement this kind of vision in the next couple of decades, the Christian community must be able to work together on the issue of poverty. We need to follow the lead of organizations like Call to Renewal, a faith-based movement to overcome poverty that has been able to draw together a vast range of Christians from Catholic, mainline Protestant, and the historic black and Latino and white evangelical circles.

> *It is realistic to think that a biblically based vision could become widely influential and dramatically reduce poverty in the next decade.*

I am convinced that Christians in the United States have an historic opportunity to work together to empower the poor. It is realistic to think that a biblically based, empirically grounded holistic vision, and strategies that include faith-based approaches, could become widely influential and dramatically reduce poverty in the next decade. That will only happen, however, if a large movement of Christians and other citizens join around a common vision and agenda. That can only happen if we are ready to work hard and sacrifice narrow self-interest. That can only happen if God mysteriously blesses us with inner renewal and spiritual revival that transforms millions of comfortable Christian materialists into passionate champions of the poor.

We have more material resources than ever before. Tragically, we are also more materialistic and more focused on individual self-fulfillment. Will we take the path of generosity and justice? Or will we slip slowly into ever-greater self-gratification?

The path of self-indulgence defies God and threatens democracy. A large number of poor, angry, disenfranchised youth with no stake in society and no hope for the future live in the heart of all our great cities. Unless we end their agony, they will shatter our comfort. On the other hand, if enough Christians and others of goodwill join together with a new holistic vision and strategy, we could end the scandal of widespread poverty in the richest nation in history.

QUESTIONS FOR DISCUSSION

1. What information or statistics from this article did you find the most surprising?

2. In what ways have you personally seen poor families struggle to make ends meet?

3. How would you define justice—in your own words?

4. Consider the roles that the government, general public (media, businesses, etc.), and faith-based organizations play in transforming the lives of the poor. What do you consider the strengths and weaknesses of each group's role?

5. In which of the five critical areas mentioned by the author do you think you are most likely to be a world changer? (Living wage, renewed two-parent families, health care for everyone, schools that work, justice and faith in action.) Be prepared to explain your reasons.

REFERENCES

The following websites and articles provide information, data, and statistics related to the issues of poverty, policy, and justice referred to in this article.

Websites
Call to Renewal; A faith-based movement to overcome poverty:
    http://www.calltorenewal.com/
Economic and Labor Statistics. U.S. Department of Labor: Bureau of Labor Statistics:
    http://www.bls.gov/
Fragile Family and Child Wellbeing Study; Bendheim-Thomas Center for Research on
    Child Wellbeing, Woodrow Wilson School of Public and International Affairs,
    Princeton University: http://crcw.princeton.edu/fragilefamilies/
Joint Center for Poverty Research; Northwestern University/University of Chicago:
    http://www.jcpr.org/
Statistics on Wealth Inequality in America:
    http://www.worldrevolution.org/Projects/Features/Inequality/USInequalityhtm
Trends in CEO pay. AFL-CIO: http://www.aflcio.org/corporateamerica/paywatch/
United States Department of Health & Human Services Poverty Guidelines:
    http://www.hhs.gov/
U.S. Census Bureau Statistics on Poverty: http://www.census.gov/hhes/www/poverty.html

Articles and Reports
Center on Budget and Policy Priorities. 2005. States' Vehicle Asset Policies In The Food
Stamp Program. http://www.cbpp.org/7-30-01fa.htm
Food Security Institute Center on Hunger and Poverty. 2003. Hunger and Food
Insecurity Among the Elderly. The Heller Graduate School for Social Policy and
Management. http://www.centeronhunger.org/pdf/Elderly.pdf.
Scommegna, Paola. 2005. Many Unwed Low-Income Parents in U.S. Need Both
    Relationship Skills and Employment Programs. Population Reference Bureau.
    http://www.prb.org/Template.cfm?Section=PRB&template=/Content/ContentGroups
    /05_Articles/Many_Unwed_Low-Income_Parents_in_U_S__Need_Both_
    Relationship_Skills_and_Employment_Programs.htm.
The Distribution Of Wealth In America. n.d. http://www.faculty.fairfield.edu/faculty/
    hodgson/Courses/so11/stratification/income&wealth.htm.
U.S. Census Bureau Report. 2004. Income, Poverty, and Health Insurance Coverage in
    the United States: 2003. http://www.census.gov/prod/2004pubs/p60-226.pdf.
U.S. Congress. Senate. Science, Technology and Space Subcommittee of the Committee
on Commerce, Science, and Transportation. The Effects of Marriage and Divorce on
    Families and Children. Presented by Gordon Berlin in May 2004,
    http://www.mdrc.org/publications/386/testimony.html.
UAW Research Bulletin. 2004. CEO Pay 2003.
    http://uaw.org/resrch/04/123004ceopay03.pdf.

Other Books

Carter, Stephen. 1993. *The culture of disbelief: How American law and politics trivialize religious devotion.* New York: Basic Books.

Gordon, Wayne. 1995. *Real hope in Chicago.* Grand Rapids, MI: Zondervan.

Harrington, Michael. 1962. *The other America: Poverty in the United States.* New York: Macmillan.

Murray, Charles. 1984. *Losing ground: American social policy 1950-1980.* New York: Basic Books.

Olasky, Marvin. 1995. *The tragedy of American compassion.* Washington, D.C.: Regnery Publishing.

The Politics of Health Care & Poverty

by John Marty and Connie Marty

Summary: U.S. government policies and political decisions have a major impact on the public's health and welfare. John and Connie Marty raise questions about the increasing number of Americans who struggle to pay for health care, examine significant issues of a system that is inaccessible for one in seven people in the country, and summarize the options for health care reform.

> The U.S. health care system has some of the best-trained health care professionals, some of the most advanced technology and some of the finest health care facilities in the world. Yet despite all of these incredible pluses, one cannot deny that our health care system fails to meet the needs of the poor and uninsured. We must ask ourselves why this is so.

When nurses, doctors, or other health professionals think about improving health care, chances are that politics or government policies are not foremost on their minds. Yet, political decisions made by all levels of government have a major impact on virtually every aspect of our health care system.

Health care public policy in the United States is far different from most other western, industrialized nations. Whether one supports these health policies or not, they are not very kind to the poor, especially for those with significant medical needs. Equally troubling is that American health care policies have the impact of driving even more people into poverty.

How Do We Compare To Other Countries?

The United States health care system is not cheap. In 2002, the U.S. spent (combining private and public expenditures) an average of over $5200 per person on health care, which is 34% higher than Switzerland, the next most costly country, and a whopping 80% more than the $2931 Canadians spend per person (OECD Health Data 2004a). Despite high expenditures, the United States ranks worse on basic health indicators, such as infant mortality and life expectancy, than virtually all of the west

Connie Marty and John Jaarsma Marty live in Roseville, Minnesota with their two children. Connie works for the "Ending Poverty Initiative" of the Saint Paul Area Synod of the ELCA (Lutheran) church. She is a former board member of Bread for the World. John is a state senator known for his work in government ethics and campaign finance reform. He has a strong interest in health care as well as in fighting environmental risks to public health. Senator Marty is author of legislation to require universal health care regardless of which policy model Minnesota politicians choose to follow.

European countries, Japan, and Canada (OECD Health Data 2004b). Although other industrialized nations spend fewer dollars per person, they are able to provide universal health care for all of their citizens, while 45 million Americans—one of every seven people—lack health insurance (DeNavas-Walt, Proctor, and Mills 2004).

How Does This Impact The Poor?

Many low-income Americans cannot afford to go to the doctor or pay for needed medical procedures or prescriptions. The elderly poor especially cannot afford to pay for in-home medical care or help with cooking and chores as they recuperate from illness or surgery.

The inability to pay for health care is not only a problem for those without insurance, but also for many with coverage. Many of the poor have health insurance through government programs, chiefly from Medicaid and Medicare. But few health plans, public or private, offer comprehensive benefits, and virtually all require significant co-payments and deductibles. So even with health insurance, many families find health care unaffordable.

As health care costs rise, politicians and employers often try to save money by moving towards "stripped-down plans so riddled with co-payments, deductibles and exclusions that serious illness leads straight to bankruptcy," according to Dr. Steffie Woolhandler, a Harvard University physician who supports universal health coverage (CNN/Money 2005, ¶15).

Dr. Woolhandler claims that illness frequently leads to bankruptcy, even for many insured patients, and that, "covering the uninsured isn't enough. We must also upgrade and guarantee continuous coverage for those who have insurance" (CNN/Money 2005, ¶14).

Woolhandler participated in a study that showed that about half of all bankruptcies filed in the United States are caused by medical bills. These medical-expense-related bankruptcies affect about two million people when you include the dependents of the adult filing. Among families whose illnesses led to bankruptcy, out-of-pocket costs averaged almost $12,000 over the course of the illness. Most of these people (76%) had insurance when they became ill, with the costs coming from co-pays and deductibles. In addition, many lost their health insurance coverage due to the illness. The results of this study demonstrated a direct relationship between illness and bankruptcy (Himmelstein et al. 2005).

> One in seven people lack any health insurance, and an even greater percentage have coverage that requires such large out-of-pocket payments that one illness or injury could easily bankrupt them.

Public opinion polls consistently show that few political issues are as important to the public as the affordability of health care. This is not surprising when one in seven people lack any health insurance, and an even greater percentage have coverage that requires such large out-of-pocket payments that one illness or injury could easily bankrupt them. On top of the large numbers of un- and under-insured people, many more are just a lay-off, a divorce, or an accident away from losing the coverage they have.

With so many Americans too poor to pay for health care (or, since many are middle class, perhaps it is more accurate to say they are "not rich enough"), it is surprising that citizens are not up-in-arms about the political policies that have brought us to this point. Perhaps many do not understand the connection between public policy and their trouble with medical bills.

People who struggle to pay, or cannot pay for health care, rarely receive preventive care; they frequently ignore health problems, seeking treatment only when the problem becomes too serious to ignore. It is not unheard of for low-income parents to avoid taking their child to the doctor for an ear infection until it is so severe that it causes permanent hearing loss. Several years ago, we met the widow of a man who cut his heart medication pills in half, not because he was supposed to, but because he could not afford the refills and he wanted to make his supply last longer. Whether his failure to take the prescribed dose caused his death cannot be known. But it is clear that the inability to pay can have fatal results. In 2004, the National Academy of Science estimated that the lack of health coverage results in about 18,000 deaths per year in the U.S.—six times as many people as died in the September 11th attacks (IOM 2004, ¶6)!

> *Failure to take advantage of preventive care might appear to save money in the short run, but can result in far more expensive care in the long run.*

Unfortunately, lack of health care is not the only problem facing low-income Americans. Over 36 million people are "food insecure," meaning that they do not know whether their groceries will last until

> **Bread for the World Institute:**
> Seeks justice for hungry people by engaging in research and education on policies related to hunger and development.
> http://www.bread.org/index.html

their next paycheck. Many Americans frequently skip meals, sometimes not eating for a whole day because they cannot afford enough food (Bread for the World 2005). Obviously, it is more difficult to stay healthy when eating an inadequate diet.

Why Is U.S. Health Care So Expensive?

Families are not the only ones struggling with the high cost of health care. Employers that are attempting to provide health benefits to employees struggle, as do government agencies that are attempting to cover the uninsured. Everybody is hurting from the rapidly escalating costs of medical care, and they are seeking answers.

In the U.S., we spend almost 15% of our gross domestic product on health care. That is over $2000 higher per person, every year, than economically competitive nations spend. If our health care system does not produce better results than those countries, why is it so expensive?

Overuse Of The Health Care System

One common perspective politicians or businesses have on the problem of skyrocketing medical costs is that they are paying too much for health care because we consume too much of it. The obvious solution, from this perspective, is to reduce the amount of health care provided. Thus, employers reduce the number of employees to whom they offer health benefits, and they require their covered workers to pay more of the cost through co-payments and deductibles.

Federal and state governments with this viewpoint take a similar approach regarding Medicaid and Medicare, reducing the number of people who qualify for coverage, and requiring individuals and families to pick up more of the cost. However, this approach frequently does nothing more than shift the costs to others. For example, a couple of years ago, the state of Minnesota made budget cuts to balance the state budget. Among the "savings" proposed was a $1000 co-payment for low-income adults who were hospitalized. Because most of the adults who would qualify for the coverage earned only about a thousand dollars per month (even less when they were hospitalized and couldn't work) they would be unable to afford their $1000 co-pay. As a result, hospitals would have received a thousand dollars less from the state for each low-income adult patient, and been left with the futile task of trying to collect money from people who didn't have any. In the end, hospitals would have had to swallow their losses, or pass the bulk of them on to paying patients and insurers through even higher health care costs.

Certainly, overuse can be a major cause of soaring health care costs. This can happen when patients demand, or physicians promote, unnecessary tests. Overuse may also stem from situations where physician groups or hospitals own expensive equipment, such as MRI scanners, and it is in their financial interest to order more of the expensive tests using this equipment. It also happens when physicians or nurses practice "defensive medicine" by ordering excessive tests and procedures, against their best medical judgment, in order to reduce their risk of being sued. Ironically, in spite of undue caution, some specialists, such as obstetricians, still find malpractice insurance incredibly expensive—an expense that they must add to their patient charges.

Underuse Of The Health Care System

While there is some overuse of the health care system, most people try to stay away from the doctor whenever possible. Perhaps a more significant reason for high health care costs is underuse of the system in terms of preventive health care. Failure to take advantage of preventive care might appear to save money in the short run, but can result in far more expensive care in the long run.

Decreasing public health budgets, along with the growing number of people who are uninsured, or who cannot afford insurance's significant out-of-pocket costs, have led to a decrease in preventive health behaviors. Others underuse the health care system by skipping visits to the doctor or choosing not to fill prescriptions. The shortage of influenza vaccinations in the winter of 2004-05 exemplified the potential effects of underuse of the medical system. In good years, many people who should get flu shots do not get them due to the cost or indifference. The lack of vaccines exacerbated this problem by encouraging even more people to forgo this important preventive measure. This under-utilization of the flu vaccine led to the potential of costly care for preventable cases of the flu.

The first step towards health care cost containment ought to be to give everyone, especially children, access to preventive health care. This could potentially save more than just health care dollars. Giving all children vision and hearing screenings could save large amounts of special education costs by reducing the number of students whose learning is hampered by unrecognized vision and hearing problems.

While virtually every politician talks about his or her concern for children, many are unwilling to pay the cost of providing this care, even if it saves money over the long haul. Perhaps one of the secrets to the lower health care costs of other countries is that universal coverage often focuses more intentionally on preventive care.

> Despite all of these incredible pluses, one cannot deny that our health care system fails to meet the needs of the poor and uninsured.

Big Profits

Not everyone is hurting financially in our current health care system. While many people who have jobs in the health care field do not even have health care coverage for themselves, some people have made good money providing health care, health insurance, or prescription drugs. The 25 highest-paid executives of 10 large health insurance plans earned a total of over $200 million in 2000. That is an average of over $8 million per executive! One CEO of a large health corporation earned over $54 million that year (Pollack, Woods, and O'Rourke 2001, 6). Even nonprofit hospital systems can be quite profitable for some executives, with one executive earning $7.4 million (Nonprofit Hospital 2004).

Boston University researchers have estimated that over 60 percent of the federal government's new expenditures for prescription drugs under the 2003 Medicare legislation will end up as additional profits for drug manufacturers. "This windfall means an estimated $139 billion dollars in increased profits over eight years for the world's most profitable industry" (Sager and Socolar 2003, 7). This is not money used for drug research, but profits they receive *after* all expenditures for research and development. The federal government, not the drug manufacturers, pays for much of the research for new prescription drugs. In many other countries, government regulations prevent excessive profits, but in the U.S., regulations often make those profits higher. The 2003 Medicare "Reform" legislation actually prohibits the government from negotiating for lower prices, thereby guaranteeing that manufacturers will get the price they want.

There are bound to be disagreements over how government can reduce health care costs, but some policies and practices deserve to be questioned by nurses and health care workers. How do some people make so much money off a health care system that is too expensive for one in every seven Americans? Why are the concerns of the American public so disconnected from the policies established by their elected officials? Why is the political debate over health care reform so powerfully influenced by constant pressure from various companies involved in the health care business? Why

do heavy lobbying and generous campaign contributions from executives in the health care field help to insure that their voices are heard in Washington and in state capitols, when the voices of the poor are seldom if ever heard?

Why Is The U.S. Health Care System So Ineffective For The Poor?

As a nation, we have the potential resources to care for all of our people, including the poor. Our citizens have been known for opening their hearts when they come face to face with someone who is suffering. Many health professionals, working in nonprofit clinics, dedicate their careers to serving the uninsured and the poor. Some do so for religious reasons. Christians do so in response to Christ's message: "for I was hungry and you gave me food...I was sick and you took care of me...truly I tell you, just as you did it to one of the least of these who are members of my family, you did it to me" (Matthew 25:35, 36, 40 NRSV). In fact, a large number of hospitals around the country were founded by various denominations, most by the Roman Catholic Church; many were staffed by nuns who received little compensation for their service. People from a wide range of faiths choose to serve the poor for religious reasons or out of simple human compassion.

The U.S. health care system also has some of the best-trained health care professionals, some of the most advanced technology, and some of the finest health care facilities in the world. Yet, despite all of these incredible pluses, one cannot deny that our health care system fails to meet the needs of the poor and uninsured. We must ask ourselves why this is so.

From a political perspective, one of the main reasons is that the poor do not have much of a voice in government. They have no lobbyists to fight for them in the politi-

> Escalating health care costs are forcing businesses, politicians, and consumers to face the fact that our current trends are not sustainable; therefore, change is both necessary and inevitable.

cal system, as do the executives in the health industry.

Furthermore, politicians rarely hear the public clamoring for more spending on health care, especially for the poor. This may come from the common attitude that many of the poor are lazy and undeserving. It can be difficult to understand the challenges others face. We may not realize that many "poor" people do work full-time, sometimes working more than one job, yet cannot afford medical care. We may not realize that other "poor" people are unemployed or are only able to work part time due to mental illness, physical disability, or chronic pain, since they look "normal" to us.

It is easier to open our hearts when we come face to face with an individual who is suffering, but harder to show sympathy for anonymous masses. From a distance, we don't see hurting people, we see statistics; we don't want our tax dollars spent on nameless, faceless statistics. However, as growing numbers of middle-income families struggle to pay for health care, the pain and the affordability problem has touched many more people and pressure for government reform is slowly building.

Prospects For Health Care Reform

Many nurses and other health care professionals who see the needs of the poor and uninsured in their daily practice understand that there are gaps in the system that need to be addressed. Escalating health care costs are forcing businesses, politicians, and consumers to face the fact that our current trends are not sustainable; therefore, change is both necessary and inevitable. So what are the prospects for change? Following this article is a summary of some of the most common options.

What Is Next for Health Care And The Poor?

Most low- and moderate-income people don't know or care which of the models politicians choose for health care. They only know that the current system is not working for them; they cannot afford to pay for a visit to the doctor or to pay for the prescriptions they need.

Nurses and other medical professionals are likely to find a growing number of poor people among their patients. Stories of inadequate and inconsistent care are on the rise; stories like those about women who receive a free breast cancer screening, but because of financial hardship, don't follow up with a visit to the doctor despite having a suspicious lump exposed by their mammogram.

> Many nurses and other health care professionals who see the needs of the poor and uninsured in their daily practice understand that there are gaps in the system that need to be addressed.

The various models for change in health care delivery described above will continue to be the focus of political debate in Washington and in state capitols. The poor will most likely become worse off if the focus of these debates is on cost containment and overuse of health care rather than prevention and the needs of the poor. If there is no reversal of the rapid rise in health care costs and growth in the number of uninsured and underinsured people, more people will likely become poor because of health care costs.

Political Awareness Of Medical Professionals

Nurses' roles and responsibilities encompass assisting the healthy in maintaining their health, as well as helping the sick towards healing and/or a better quality of life. Nurses' vocation, their calling, is to show compassion as they work with their patients one at a time.

But much of the health and well being of medical patients is influenced by health care policy determined through our nation's political system. Regardless of which political party or political philosophy a health professional adheres to, it is important that he or she pay attention to the politics of health care, and push for policies to ensure their patients have access to the care they need. After all, this is a democracy, and we citizens have a right and a responsibility to be involved in our government.

> *The poor will most likely become worse off if the focus of these debates is on cost containment and overuse of health care rather than prevention and the needs of the poor.*

QUESTIONS FOR DISCUSSION

1. What information or statistics from this article did you find the most surprising?

2. Imagine you have an opportunity to meet with your State Representative and State Senator about government and health care issues. Make a list of questions and priority issues you would like to address during this meeting.

3. Do the same for a potential meeting with your U.S. Representative and Senator.

4. In what ways have you seen overuse and or underuse of the U.S. healthcare system?

5. The authors conclude, "This is a democracy, and we citizens have a right and a responsibility to be involved in our government." Specify one way you can become more involved in government issues related to healthcare and poverty.

6. Below the author presents three models of health care reform. Read through the models. Which model do you favor? Be prepared to explain your reasons.

THE TRADITIONAL COST CONTAINMENT, PERSONAL RESPONSIBILITY MODEL

Proposals of this model include:

• Making it more difficult to sue for malpractice or medical errors. Americans go to court more frequently than people in other countries, and many politicians believe that fear of lawsuits is forcing doctors to practice "defensive medicine," ordering unnecessary tests and procedures to prevent lawsuits.

• Shifting more costs to the patient. If people are responsible for more of the costs of their care, they will not seek medical treatment as often, but only when it is absolutely necessary.

• Selling high-deductible insurance with health savings accounts. With high deductibles, the health plan doesn't cost as much and if consumers put money into a savings account, they can pay for coverage below the deductible amount.

• Relying on competition to drive down prices. If you give people more price information, they can compare costs and quality of service, and will shop around to find less expensive doctors and hospitals.

• Creating big purchasing alliances. If businesses join together, they can have more purchasing clout in negotiating prices from health plans and providers.

• Allowing health insurers to offer stripped-down plans that cover fewer things and have more exclusions so they can be less expensive.

This is the most popular model of health reform in American politics. Proponents claim it will save money by reducing the number of medical procedures performed. Critics suggest that this has been tried in the past, has not done anything to restrain costs, and that it leaves many people with little or no health care coverage.

THE "MEDICARE FOR ALL" UNIVERSAL HEALTH CARE MODEL

Proposals of this model include:

• The government would replace the health insurance companies and health plans, and as is currently the case under Medicare, it would negotiate rates and pay the medical bills to private sector health care providers. This would reduce administrative expenses from billing and paperwork by avoiding the costs of marketing health plans to various groups, and by eliminating the need for a provider to bill numerous insurers and individuals.

• Patients would choose their doctors and clinics rather than be limited to certain providers.

• The plan would provide comprehensive benefits including dental, mental health, and long-term care.

• The plan would give everyone access to preventive care, saving money by addressing problems before they become more serious and expensive to treat.

• There would be no cost-shifting caused by uncompensated care, and the plan would eliminate price disparities between consumers.

• Overuse of expensive technology would be prevented by planning how much of such equipment is needed in a community. Currently, several hospitals in a community might purchase expensive MRI scanners not because of need, but to compete with other hospitals.

• Depending on the design of the plan, there might or might not be some co-payments for consumers.

This model is the most similar to other industrialized countries and would require the biggest change from our current system. It is not very popular among politicians or the business community. Critics suggest that people might be forced to wait a long time for elective procedures, that it will reduce the quality of health care available, and will cost more. Critics also contend that people will have less choice and fewer options in their care with these models and might seek treatment in other countries. The model has a strong, though small, following among some nurses and doctors and some consumer groups.

THE EFFICIENCY AND "BEST PRACTICES" MODEL

Proposals of this model include:

• Developing "best practices" models for medical treatment. If certain protocols are more effective than others, doctors would be expected to use the more effective procedures instead of the ones they are currently using.

• Creating big purchasing alliances. If businesses join together, they can have more purchasing clout in negotiating prices from health plans and providers. This option is common to the traditional cost-containment model.

• Requiring larger businesses to provide benefits to full-time employees, or at least offer incentives to employers to help them do so.

• Expanding the number of people covered under health plans, if necessary, through state health care plans that receive some public funding.

• Providing coverage to all children. This is a variation of the previous point, because children without preventive care are at greater risk for long-term health and development problems than adults without coverage.

• Gathering more information from providers about price and outcomes so that consumers can shop around for the best deal.

This model falls somewhere between the first two options. It has almost as many political proponents as the first model, and many public officials support some aspects of each. Critics who support the traditional cost containment model argue that this model is too costly because it covers too many people and requires health plans to provide more complete coverage, making it more expensive. Critics who favor the universal health care model point out that this model leaves many people without coverage, and fails to gain savings on administrative costs and preventive care.

REFERENCES

Bread for the World Institute. 2005. Hunger Basics. http://www.bread.org/hungerbasics/index.html.

CNN/Money. 2005. Study: Health costs spur bankruptcy. Reuters, courtesy of CNN/*Money*, February 2. http://money.cnn.com/2005/02/02/pf/debt/health_bankruptcy.reut/?cnn=yes.

DeNavas-Walt, C., B. D. Proctor, and R. J. Mills. 2004. Income, poverty, and health insurance coverage in the United States: 2003. http://www.census.gov/prod/2004pubs/p60-226.pdf.

Institute Of Medicine Of The National Academies (IOM). 2004. The uninsured are sicker and die sooner. http://www.iom.edu/Object.File/Master/17/748/0.pdf.

Himmelstein, D., E. Warren, D. Thorne, D., and S. Woolhandler. 2005. MarketWatch: Illness and injury as contributors to bankruptcy. *Health Affairs* [Online], February 2. http://content.healthaffairs.org/cgi/content/full/hlthaff.w5.63/DC1.

Nonprofit Hospital CEO Compensation. 2004. http://www.everybodyinnobodyout.org/FAQ/datHospCEOs.htm.

OECD Health Data. 2004a. Chart 3: Health expenditure per capita, US$PPP, 2002. http://www.oecd.org/dataoecd/3/62/31938359.pdf.

OECD Health Data. 2004b. Table 1 and Table 2. http://www.oecd.org/document/16/0,2340,en_2649_33929_2085200_1_1_1_1,00.html.

Pollack, R., J. Woods, J., and L. O'Rourke. 2001. Healthy pay for health plan executives. *Families USA*, June. http://www.familiesusa.org/site/DocServer/hmo_ceo.pdf?docID=761.

Sager, A., and D. Socolar. 2003. 61 percent of Medicare's new prescription drug subsidy is windfall profit to drug makers. Boston: Boston University School of Public Health. http://www.bu.edu/dbin/sph/departments/health_services/documents/health_reform/Medicare_Rx_bill_windfallprofit.pdf.

A Holistic Community Approach to Caring for the Poor

by Bruce G. Jackson

Summary: New and creative models of health care delivery are essential in overcoming the unique barriers faced in providing health care for the poor. Jackson describes some effective community models and highlights key points that make their approaches successful.

Over fifteen years ago, I moved into the inner city of Pittsburgh with my family. We lived in the shadow of a major tertiary care hospital, yet I was amazed to find I could not secure a doctor to provide primary medical care for my family. I had health insurance; if I could not find primary care in my immediate community for my family, what opportunities were available to those who had no insurance? I discovered from my neighbors, most of who were poor and uninsured, that the emergency room was their only option for health care. As I lived in the community and heard the needs of my neighbors, I saw a model of health care begin to develop that was effective because it emerged from among the people and allowed them to be involved. Through the development of The Northside Christian Health Center, I learned how a community-based model could help many previously underserved people.

Today, there are still many barriers to health care for the poor, not just in Pittsburgh, but also across the country, in both urban and rural areas. What can we do to break down these barriers in order to provide quality health care for the uninsured and underserved? How can communities provide adequate health care to the poor? Over the past 25 years, Christian Community Health Fellowship (CCHF) has been asking such questions and as a result, has developed a national network of people, students, and organizations committed to living out the Gospel through health care among the poor.

Through our experiences at CCH we have discovered some particular barriers to access of health care among the poor, and we have considered the positive impact of a community-based approach to overcoming these barriers. The purpose of this article is to

> I saw a model of health care begin to develop that was effective because it emerged from among the people and allowed them to be involved.

Bruce Jackson, MA, is executive director of Christian Community Health Fellowship. Prior to this he lived 19 years in Pittsburgh's inner city where he was on the staff at Allegheny Center Alliance Church, serving in the capacities of Counselor, family and community ministries, Executive Pastor, and Director of Community Development. While in Pittsburgh he helped initiate the North Side Christian Health Center, offering primary health care, and then served as its Executive Director.

CHRISTIAN COMMUNITY HEALTH FELLOWSHIP

Vision: Living Out the Gospel through Health Care for the Poor

The three fundamental goals of CCHF are to:

1. Help provide quality health care for the poor through recruiting and empowering Christian health care workers for this important task;
2. Function as a forum to raise and discuss questions related to this vision;
3. Create opportunities for health care professionals and students to meet and share stories for mutual education, support, and fellowship.

CCHF Provides:
• Publications
• Planning and/or supporting conferences
• Opportunities for students to obey the biblical mandate of serving among the poor
• Technical assistance to health centers interested in starting up
• Evaluating programs
• Replicating Best Practices programs

http://www.cchf.org/

identify some of the barriers to health care and barriers to improvement in people's overall lives, and to describe how a focus on community building can help overcome these barriers.

Unique Barriers for the Poor

The statistics are clear—the underserved in the United States face barriers to health care that lessen their chances of receiving quality care. Some of the often-mentioned barriers include lack of health insurance, a shortage of primary care physicians in poor neighborhoods, and difficulty traveling to the point of care. However, there are also less obvious factors, including lack of options and limited assets, powerlessness and survivor mentality, and issues of trust. Nurses and other health care providers who gain a better understanding of these barriers will improve their ability to care for the poor.

Lack Of Options And Limited Assets

Most definitions of poverty focus on income levels or determinants of hunger. However, many other factors affect and influence poverty. Payne, DeVol, and Smith define poverty as "the extent to which an individual does without resources" (2001, 17). These "resources" include financial, emotional, mental, spiritual, and physical resources, support systems, relationships/role models, knowledge of hidden rules, and coping strategies. It is apparent that a lack of options contributes to the poverty of an individual or a community. The questions that arise are, "What does the lack of options do to a person and/or a community?" and "How can increasing options help?"

A discussion about options for the poor requires a balanced understanding of personal responsibility and the systemic influences that contribute to poverty. Neither is fully to blame. Clearly, individuals can make choices that will limit the options they have, and place them at a disadvantage in life. On the other hand, systemic factors such as lack of education, poor finances, decreased mobility, discrimination, environmental factors, or living location can limit options and lead to the poverty trap. Environments that minimize options generally produce impoverished conditions for entire communities, not just for individuals who live in them.

In the category of personal responsibility, poor decisions and excessive spending can lead to a person to hunger and homelessness. On the systemic side, Shipler (2004) points out how businesses can easily take advantage of the working poor and push them into debt. Check-cashing establishments levy heavy charges and often take advantage of the poor who may lack math skills or understanding of better financial choices.

We may consider it irresponsible to use the emergency room for primary medical care when better alternatives are available. However, many physicians and other health care providers refuse to practice in poverty-stricken areas because they are unprofitable due to the high number of uninsured, Medicaid, or Medicare patients. This systemic problem limits or even eliminates people's choices regarding primary care physicians, pharmacists, and other health care services.

Poverty can also be understood as the quantity of assets built into a person's life. The more assets a person has, the greater his or her ability to negotiate successfully through life. Adequate assets enable an individual to prioritize and be comfortable with delaying gratification. Such a person will be more likely to engage in preventive health care behaviors. In contrast, a person who is impoverished often finds that his or her choices are limited. When an opportunity presents itself, the individual may take full advantage of what is available at that moment, even if the choice is impractical or has poor long-term consequences. Such a person is much less likely to engage in preventive care, which has no immediate rewards.

Search Institute of Minneapolis has discovered 40 Developmental Assets that are "[the] building blocks of healthy development that help young people grow up healthy, caring, and responsible" (Search Institute 2004, Asset List). Through extensive research among 12- to 16-year-olds, the Institute found that "the greater the numbers of Developmental Assets that are experienced by young people, the more positive and successful their development. The fewer the number of assets present, the greater the possibility youth will engage in risky behaviors such as drug use, unsafe sex, and violence" (Search Institute 2004, 40 Developmental Assets). According to the Developmental Asset framework, assets can be categorized into external assets—positive and constructive roles played by families, schools, congregations, and neighborhoods, etc.—and internal assets—such as values, social competencies, and inner strength (Search Institute 2004, Introduction to Assets).

There are many ways

Communities will do well to consider developing emotional, mental, and spiritual assets, expanding support systems, and teaching coping strategies, in addition to improving physical and financial resources.

members of a community can work together to increase assets, which will consequently help people negotiate through life in a more positive and successful manner and help them avoid or escape from poverty. In order to develop effective programs to improve the health of the poor, communities will do well to consider developing emotional, mental, and spiritual assets, expanding support systems, and teaching coping strategies, in addition to improving physical and financial resources.

Powerlessness & The Survivor Mentality

Yet another way to define poverty is powerlessness that leads to the survivor mentality. People living in poverty generally feel they have little power to control their lives or make long-term choices and the best they can do is react to the most pressing need in their lives that day, that hour, that minute. When an urgent problem arises, it demands their immediate attention and assumes priority over everything else in their life. This is a survivor mentality. Lack of control is a powerful inhibitor that often brings a sense of hopelessness to a person.

> In survivor mentality, a person feels there is little margin for error, so he or she focuses only on what will get him or her through that day.

In survivor mentality, a person feels there is little margin for error due to a lack of resources, finances, and the opportunity to maneuver through life, so he or she focuses only on what will get him or her through that day. If eviction is an imminent threat, a person operating from a survivor mentality will invest all of his or her time, energy, and money in paying the rent rather than in paying for health care needs, even if he or she has significant health issues.

Survivor mentality helps to explain why people often deal with their health care needs on an emergency basis rather than from a preventive one. It is not because they don't want to prevent health problems. Impoverished people are aware of health concerns as they experience the deaths of family members, friends, and neighbors due to heart attacks, cancer, diabetes, and violence. But, overwhelmed by so many other concerns, they usually can give little attention to preventive care.

Health care centers in poorer communities often experience high no-show rates for appointments, because people in survival mode do not have an appointment mentality. They do not lead carefully programmed lives with timely appointments and meetings. Instead, they schedule their lives according to whatever need is urgent for that day. This mentality makes it difficult for people to schedule and show up for regular or preventive health care appointments.

New models of health care in impoverished communities need to consider throwing out the traditional appointment-in-advance approach. Health care providers who develop creative approaches for these situations will be more successful. For example, some health care centers now use a same-day schedule system that allows people to call for an appointment that day. So far, this system seems to reduce the no-show rate and allows an individual quick access to the provider.

Issues Of Trust

Trust is another unspoken barrier to health care for the poor. People caught in poverty face rejection during many of their daily encounters. Other social issues in their neighborhoods create environments of distrust. If patients do not feel they can trust a doctor, nurse, or other health care provider, they will avoid the encounter altogether. They need to know that the provider cares for them and is concerned about them.

Historically, trust developed in a physician-patient relationship through personal encounters with the same physician over time. But when rotating volunteers provide care in free clinics, it is hard to establish physician-patient trust. When clinic hours are limited and income guidelines for acceptance are confusing, it is difficult to maintain confidence, continuity, compliance, or trust. In order to see the volume of people needing care, providers may appear rushed and impersonal with patients, and may unknowingly communicate a lack of caring. Patients may feel the doctors, nurses, and other staff are not interested in them, and will begin to question whether they can trust the providers. As Keis, DeGeus, Cashman, and Savageua note, free clinics play an important role in the provision of health care to uninsured and underserved populations; however, the great need for free clinics highlight "a system that is failing a significant proportion of its citizens" (2004, 612-613).

Attitudes of the health care providers and staff of an organization and the atmosphere they create can affect trust as well. People know when health care providers are treating them as an inconvenience or nuisance because they are poor. They often already feel bad about themselves because they cannot pay for services; they may forgo care until it is absolutely necessary because of anticipation that they will not be welcomed or given quality care.

Imagine you are treated impersonally when you arrive for an appointment, then after a long wait, you encounter a provider who is distracted by busyness. This can easily create a negative impression. A patient may view the encounter as typical of the way a poor person is treated and cared for. Psychology calls this dynamic projection. A person projects his or her negative perspective of how a person in authority will treat him or her onto a care provider. I have seen this take place even when the provider is very compassionate. Providers cannot prevent the patient from such projections; however, they can attempt to minimize them by developing a welcoming and accepting atmosphere. Improving levels of trust in the process of providing health care to the poor will likely improve overall health outcomes.

In the movie *Patch Adams*, there is a moving moment when the instructor is taking the medical students through the hospital on rounds. As the group encounters a patient, the instructor began to describe the woman's condition. Great concern comes across the woman's face as she listens to the discussion and the students' questions. At that moment, Patch Adams appears from behind the medical students. He quietly asks the instructor, "What is the patient's name?" The instructor, looking baffled, peers down at the chart and calls out the name. Patch then looks at the woman and softly says, "Hello Margarie." In an instant, her anxiety is gone. This scene speaks of the importance of the development of trust and acceptance in patient care.

A Holistic Community Approach To Caring For The Poor

Community Health Centers (CHC) have become the preferred vehicle for care of the uninsured and underinsured in the United States, strongly supported by the Department of Health and Human Services. A CHC is a full-time, primary care facility available to patients of all ages. A patient is able to choose a provider who will offer continuity of care. Additional services such as dental and mental health care, social work consultations, and pharmacies are often provided at CHCs as well. CHCs usually accept insurance as well as Medicare and Medicaid. For those with no or limited insurance, there is a sliding scale fee based upon the federal poverty guidelines. These centers remove financial barriers for patients while maintaining continuity of care.

> However, people's health care needs cannot be addressed in isolation from these community-based concerns.

The movement of Christian Community Development, promoted by John Perkins and Wayne Gordon, has helped to model the need for a holistic approach focused on caring for the whole person emotionally, spiritually, physically, socially, financially, and every other "-ally." This approach strives to understand the impoverished community by becoming part of the community and joining the people in their concerns regarding injustice, economics, health care, education, employment, family life, and housing. This list of issues can seem overwhelming. However, people's health care needs cannot be addressed in isolation from these community-based concerns. Effective health care for the underserved needs to be provided in terms of the community context.

An excellent model of a community approach is found in Lawndale, a neighborhood on Chicago's west side. The neighborhood has been greatly enhanced by the presence of Lawndale Community Church, which has been a major force in addressing the needs of the area and providing Christian community using a holistic approach to bring help and healing into people's lives. The church has not only helped the community establish a health center, but has addressed numerous other issues of poverty through a community development corporation, businesses, housing, education programs, and employment training. Family members, neighbors, and local churches and organizations are encouraged to work together to support one another.

Lawndale Christian Health Center (LCHC) is accredited by the Joint Commission on Accreditation of Health Care Organizations (JCAHO), and is recognized as a Federally Qualified Health Center (FQHC) by the U.S. Department of Health and Human Services' Bureau of Primary Health Care. Their mission is "to show and share the love of Jesus Christ to the Lawndale and Garfield Communities by providing holistic, affordable, and quality health care services" (Lawndale n.d.).

The Center sees 80,000 patients per year and provides primary care and health management, dental and eye clinics, obstetrics, pediatrics, and ancillary services such as laboratory, radiology, and pharmacy. Special services offer care for targeted populations such as asthmatics, diabetics, and persons with HIV. The holistic approach of LCHC includes pastoral care, school outreach, and nutrition programs (Lawndale n.d.).

Health care models built on approaches like that of LCHC build assets, options, and respect for the people in the community. They are successful because they break down barriers, and provide care that emerges from among the residents and involves them in development and leadership, rather than care that is brought in for the residents, and is distant, out of touch, and often condescending.

When ministries and services are developed within a community and providers are involved in the community, they are also more likely to address concerns for preventive care. Health screenings, education, and support groups focused on healthy lifestyles and changed behaviors can be presented in the context of public gatherings, church services, and community events. For example, in such settings, older men and women can come alongside young men and women to teach them how to be godly men and women, which can lead to a reduction in teenage pregnancies. In these ways, community-based models lead to long-term as well as short-term improvements in health care.

Holistic community models can offer the most effective care for the poor and help to overcome the multi-faceted problems and unique barriers that impoverished communities face. Nurses and other health care providers who work to develop community-based models that increase options, build assets, empower the people served, and create trusting relationships will improve their ability to care for the poor.

QUESTIONS FOR DISCUSSION

1. The author states, "In order to develop effective programs to improve the health of the poor, communities will do well to consider developing emotional, mental, and spiritual assets, expanding support systems, and teaching coping strategies, in addition to improving physical and financial resources."

   a. Which of these resources poses the biggest challenge in your community?

   b. Which of these resources are available in your community?
      Describe where/how they are available.

2. Picture your current clinical setting and imagine you are dealing with an impoverished patient who does not trust you. Describe how you would respond to him/her.

3. Discuss the health care system changes proposed by the author (same day schedules, attitudes, location, models of delivery). Do you agree or disagree that health care providers need to be willing to change and create new models in order to provide health care to the poor?

4. What can be done to encourage models like Lawndale Christian Health Center in more communities around the country?

REFERENCES

Shipler, D. K. 2004. *The working poor: Invisible in America.* New York: Knopf.

Search Institute. 2004. 40 Developmental Assets. http://www.search-institute.org/assets/.

Payne, R., P. DeVol, T. Smith. 2001. *Bridges out of poverty.* Highlands, TX: aha! Process, Inc.

Lawndale Christian Health Center. n.d. http://www.lawndale.org/default.htm.

Keis, DeGeus, Cashman, and Savageau. 2004. Characteristics of three free clinics. *Journal of Health Care for the Poor and Underserved* 15 (4): 612-613.

Overcoming Cultural Barriers in Health Care

by Jessica Escobar

Summary: Minority groups, including refugees and immigrants, often face unique barriers to health care related to cultural issues that may result from or cause poverty. Escobar identifies some of the key cultural barriers in health care and offers suggestions for overcoming these barriers.

During my childhood, my family was poor according to the standards set by society. My parents emigrated from a foreign country to the United States in hopes of finding the elusive American dream. We lived in a small apartment, facing fears of deportation day in and day out. However, to my childish mind, I had my parents, and I was able to play and go to school—all things I associated with being "rich." My mother tells me that when I was a little girl I asked her if another little girl was poor. When she asked me why I thought that, I responded, "Because her socks were dirty." I had defined poor as being unclean rather than by some government standard or other definition.

As a health care professional, working in a variety of settings, I have learned a lot about poverty since my childhood. Poverty crosses all ages, educational levels, and cultures. Poverty is both subjective and objective. Our government sets standards that determine whether people live "below the poverty line," but poverty can also be a state of mind. Poverty is multidimensional, as are the factors that cause it. One significant dimension to poverty is the inconsistent and often unequal delivery of health care to minorities, including refugees and immigrants. This disparity in health care frequently leads to a circle of problems that prevents many of these minorities from progressing into a better way of life and leads to frustration among health care workers who are trying to help them. This article will focus on some of the particular dimensions of poverty and barriers to adequate health care among refugees, immigrants, and minority races in the United States.

> One significant dimension to poverty is the inconsistent and often unequal delivery of health care to minorities, including refugees and immigrants.

Immigrants, Refugees, and Minorities

We need to understand the terminology used when discussing diversity and culture. The word "minority" can mean a variety of

---

Jessica Escobar, MSN, APRN, BC works as a family nurse practitioner at Neighborhood Health Clinic, Inc. in Fort Wayne, IN, and also as a Diabetic Clinician. She has experience in Minority Health care, and has studied Transcultural Nursing with Madeleine Leininger. She has been a clinical instructor and preceptor for St. Francis College in Fort Wayne, IN.

things. For instance, women, children, and elderly are minorities. For this article, the word "minority" means a person of any culture other than Anglo.

Immigrants and refugees are two words that describe groups of people that have come to this country. According to the Oxford American Dictionary, to immigrate means to come as a permanent resident to a country other than one's native land. Immigrants leave their countries due to political unrest, improvement in standard of living, employment, education (student visas), or because other family lives here.

Immigrants may be here on a visa, which means that they can be here as students or as employees (if their company has transferred them here) for an indefinite amount of time.

Immigrants live here as legal residents and have made the United States their home but maintain a citizenship in another country as well.

Immigrants can be naturalized citizens, meaning that they have been residents for a period of five years or more and have chosen to become United States citizens.

Immigrants can be here illegally—which means that they have crossed the border but don't have permission to live or work here. This group of immigrants is the one that faces the most adversities and hardships in this country.

Immigrants usually leave their countries and loved ones, in search of a better life. For example, in many Latin American countries there is a vast difference between the wealthy and the poor, while the middle class is small or non-existent. Employment is scarce for those who are poor, making it difficult for parents to feed and clothe their families. This disparity often leads one member of the family to immigrate to the United States, leaving the rest of their loved ones behind. In my work as a Spanish-

---

Definitions

Culture: The learned, shared, and transmitted values, beliefs, norms, and lifeways that guide a person's thinking, decisions, and actions in patterned ways.

Cultural Care: The subjectively and objectively learned and transmitted values, beliefs, and patterned lifeways that assist, support, and facilitate or enable another individual or group to maintain their well being, to improve their human condition and lifeway, or to deal with illness, handicaps, or death.

Health: A state of well being that is culturally defined, valued, and practiced, and which reflects the ability of individuals (or groups) to perform their daily role activities in culturally expressed, beneficial, and patterned lifeways.

(Leininger 1991)

---

speaking nurse practitioner, I often encountered patients who indicated that their spouse and children have remained in another country while they are trying to make money to send back to them. I could see the hurt and burden in their eyes.

Refugees, like immigrants, leave their homeland behind to come to the U.S., but their reasons for coming are different. A refugee takes "refuge" in another country because he or she needs protection or shelter from pursuit, danger, or trouble. Refugees leave countries due to persecution (religious or political); if they don't leave their native countries they risk being killed or imprisoned.

Refugees who seek asylum in this country and are granted legal permission to be here receive some short-term assistance with resettlement. Since they are here legally, they can obtain jobs and qualify for health insurance through their employment. Illegal immigrants, on the other hand, often have to use an alias to search for a job. Even if they live and work here for years, they are not entitled to health insurance.

Minority Populations Growth Reaches Even Small Towns

According to the 2000 census, there was a tremendous growth in the minority population in the United States from 1990 to 2000. In 2000, the Hispanic population outnumbered the African-American population and had grown to become the largest minority group in the States. This growth in minority populations has had a significant impact, including in the political and policy arenas. In the elections of both 2000 and 2004, the "minority" vote became very important; both political parties were wooing the African-American and the Hispanic vote.

America's new diversity is not only happening in large coastal cities, but also in small towns across the country. One example of this can be found in the county where I live, Allen County, Indiana. In this one midwestern county live refugees and immigrants from more than fifty different countries. Those from countries such as Bosnia, Croatia, Sudan, Somalia, Afghanistan, and Iraq are likely here due to the political upheaval in their native lands. Others, from countries like Argentina, Mexico, Iran, and India perhaps have come for economic reasons or to attend an American college. The 2000 census demonstrated a greater than 100% increase of Hispanics in Allen County. Of particular note is the fact that Allen County is home to the largest gathering of refugees from the country of Burma (now called Myanmar) outside of Burma itself. The influx of refugees from Burma

has created some unique cross-cultural health care challenges for our area.

Burma has gone through years of war, oppression, and major political unrest. Many refugees here were students who were forced into the jungles of Thailand to escape persecution due to the opposing political views. In the jungle, many Burmese fell into prostitution and drug abuse. Refugees suffered malnourishment and discrimination from their neighboring country. It is not surprising that many Burmese sought asylum in other countries (United States, Australia, Canada) and left family members behind, not knowing if they would ever be reunited. The Burmese people arrived in our community with a set of physical, emotional, and cultural needs that were foreign to our health care providers, creating tremendous challenges to provide adequate care for this people group.

Coming to the United States is not a guarantee of a better way of life, better health care, better education, or a safer life for refugees and immigrants. It is therefore important for nurses across the country to devote time to learning and discussing issues pertaining to refugees and immigrants and preparing to welcome them into our communities. Refugees and immigrants often face barriers that are similar to those of the poor among other minority groups.

> Coming to the United States is not a guarantee of a better way of life, better health care, better education, or a safer life for refugees and immigrants.

The Cycle of Poverty and Disease

Diabetes, hypertension, renal disease, and cardiac disease occur with increased prevalence in minority populations. These groups are not always aware of their higher risk, and they are often undertreated for these diseases. For example, compared with the general population, certain ethnic and/or economically disadvantaged communities are disproportionately affected by diabetes (Burrows etal., 2004). It is estimated that there are between 200,000 and 400,000 new cases of diabetes per year, but millions of Hispanics may have undiagnosed diabetes (Idrogo and Mazzee 2004). Screenings are available to detect risk factors that lead to strokes, heart attacks, and renal failure, and cholesterol and blood sugar screenings are relatively inexpensive. However, access, language barriers, financial concerns, and/or lack of education may prevent minority clients from being tested.

Obesity and diabetes are becoming an epidemic affecting primarily minority patients, and the associated costs are staggering. According to the American Diabetes Association, diabetes costs nearly $100 billion in direct medical care costs and indirect costs (such as lost productivity) to the work force (Burrows etal., 2004). Why don't people take better care of themselves? The reality is that people with no health insurance—or on plans without medication coverage, as has been the case with Medicare—have great difficulty affording all that is required to treat their diabetes. A blood sugar meter to test blood sugars at home may cost $60 to $80, but the real expense is in the test strips used for daily blood sugar checks. A vial of 100 strips may cost around $80. Imagine living on a limited income and needing to check your blood sugar four times a day! The expense is monumental. One vial would only last around 25 days, not to mention syringes, needles to poke the finger, alcohol wipes, and the cost of the insulin itself.

People who cannot afford the medications and supplies to treat chronic illnesses, like diabetes, end up in the hospital with complications from improper treatment and care. Some of these complications may lead to life-long debilitating problems such as foot amputations, renal failure, dialysis, and strokes. These disabilities then lead to an inability to work, which leads to further issues with poverty and the accompanying difficulty in getting adequate health care, creating a sad circle of poverty and poor health.

In many situations, people who have chronic diseases and who are financially burdened also have educational barriers. It is difficult to educate a patient who is unable to read or has a sixth grade education. Illiteracy among poor people is a difficult issue to address; it can also cause safety concerns for the patient if he or she cannot understand the written treatment or prescription instructions.

> *The more we can provide poor people with tools to make wise, informed decisions regarding their health, the more likely we will be to help them break out of the vicious cycle.*

Breaking the Cycle— What Can You Do?

Chronic diseases cross all cultural groups and all financial circumstances—there really are no barriers when disease attacks. However, managing chronic diseases among the poor requires some creative solutions. A key to help break the cycle of poverty and poor health among people with limited resources is to make it a priority to identify, prevent, and manage the many risk factors before a major illness affects people. Knowledge is power. The more we can provide poor people with tools to make wise, informed decisions regarding their health, the more likely we will be to help them break out of the vicious cycle. Educating the poor about prevention may be challenging, but it is not impossible.

One way to provide information to the poor is by accessing their meeting places in the community, contacting leaders among minority groups, and tapping into cross-cultural community resources. Churches, schools, grocery stores, or employment

THE STORY OF JUAN

Juan was a 44-year-old from Mexico who left behind a wife and six children in a village that was closer to Guatemala than to the U. S. He lived in the U.S. for about one year, saved money, and was planning to return to Mexico in three months.

Juan suffered from high blood pressure but was unaware of this ailment. He had a massive stroke and lost the ability to communicate and to use his right hand. Due to his high blood pressure, he also developed chronic renal failure that required dialysis. He was in the hospital with no family, unable to communicate or understand the English spoken by the medical staff. Juan's physician called immigration to inform them that his patient was an illegal alien and needed to be deported.

Juan's wife came to the U.S. one week after his stroke, to care for him and take him back to Mexico. The hospital was going to assist in flying them back, but they left by bus before we could assist them. They faced a four-day trip back to Mexico by bus. We never heard if he made it to Mexico. We did find out that the nearest dialysis center to their home was two hours away.

offices are great places to distribute flyers for health care fairs, brochures on disease prevention, or information on agencies available. Minority groups tend to create their own little communities within the larger group; if these areas are targeted, a large section can be reached. For example, the Burmese and Hispanic groups in my community have several ethnic grocery stores with bulletin boards to advertise upcoming events. The Burmese community also has a group of leaders who plan social events, such as a Burmese New Year celebration, and organize their community. These leaders are a valuable resource when planning local health fairs and for providing other health-related advice. Health care providers also can tap into community agencies that work directly with people who are underprivileged and of other cultures. In my community, resources include Catholic Charities, the All Nations Friendship Center sponsored by the Lutheran Churches, and the Benito Juarez Center, an employment agency and resource center for Hispanics.

Learn about the cultures represented in your community; you will be more effective in assisting and educating minority groups on illness prevention. Be respectful of their views regarding health, illness, and treatment; you will be more respected when trying to care for them. We cannot discount that folk medicine is important to many non-Anglo people groups. Many of these folk remedies may be helpful, or at least not harmful, and could be incorporated into a plan of care along with traditional medicine practices. The key is to be aware of these practices and to learn what we can, in order to discern which practices may be kept and which might require change.

It is also important to be conscious of the costs of chronic diseases when developing a plan of care with low-income minority patients. Whether you are working in the community or discharging them from a health care facility, provide a list of community clinics where patients can receive follow-up care. Inform them of clinic locations and services available. If you are unaware of cost-effective treatments, community clinics, or financial assistance, you can contact social workers in your workplace, the social services department of a larger hospitals, or consult with local public health services. Social workers or case managers in local hospitals have more experience in finding assistance for people of limited income and may be able to guide you as to where to locate appropriate care and interpreters.

¿Habla inglés?

As our communities become more diverse, it gets harder to avoid the issue of language barriers. Whether you are a teacher, a police officer, a banker, a social worker, or a medical professional, the difficulties and dangers associated with language barriers are becoming increasingly common.

ESL (English as a Second Language) classes are important tools to help new Americans learn our main language, but people do not learn English overnight. Have you tried to learn a foreign language? How difficult was it? It is unrealistic to expect that the foreigners we encounter will be able to speak English fluently. Even those that have lived here for many years probably understand English but are unable to express themselves fully because they feel shame over their inadequacies, because of the complexity of the situation, or because they have a strong accent and are unable to say things clearly.

> The inability to communicate with patients poses tremendous safety issues in health care.

Imagine being in a foreign land. Only you and four other people speak English; everyone else speaks Spanish. Where would you go for health care? Where would you go to school? Would you feel comfortable driving if the signs were in Spanish? Would you avoid certain situations because of discomfort? Would you seek out only those that understood you?

Larger cities such as Los Angeles, Houston, Chicago, or New York are able to provide more services to immigrants because the make-up of the workforce reflects the make-up of the community. However, in smaller cities the language barriers are more difficult to overcome. The number of physicians, nurses, teachers, police officers, bankers, therapists, counselors, etc., who speak a variety of languages is limited. This poses a problem when the population of non-English speaking clients is steadily growing. When only a small number of health care providers speak an important local language, like Spanish, Bosnian, or Arabic, they may end up with a large numbers of patients seeking their care. For example, one Burmese physician practices in my area. Many of the Burmese people travel an hour to see her instead of seeking care in a local clinic.

The inability to communicate with patients poses tremendous safety issues in health care. Informed consent, medication administration, and discharge instructions must all be given in the language of the patient. If no providers speak the language, how can this be done safely? Hospitals and clinics have a legal obligation to provide interpreters (following the 1964 Civil Act Reform) but many rely on housekeepers or small children to interpret instead of hiring qualified interpreters or recruiting bilingual health care providers. Housekeepers are typically employees that speak other languages, and they can be very helpful in certain situations. However, housekeepers may not have knowledge of medical issues, their English may be limited, and there is no way to verify that they are correctly interpreting what a health care provider is informing a patient.

This issue of the quality of interpreters is significant to cross-cultural care among those with limited resources. Some people who offer their services as an interpreter require high fees. A 15-30 minute interpretation session can cost a patient $20-30. Many refugees and immigrants do not have the financial resources to use such costly interpretation services. Legally, it is the responsibility of clinics and hospitals to provide this service, but many communities struggle to provide appropriate interpretation, especially if they have a sudden influx of people from particular language groups. When the large group of Burmese refugees began arriving in Allen County, hospitals, police, and many other public services struggled to find appropriate interpreters to care for all the needs of this new people group in their midst. Until communities are better prepared, it often falls to the patient to find his or her own interpreter. If they don't have a friend or relative who can translate, they have to pay for someone to do it. I have encountered some of these so-called "interpreters" who are not very accurate.

Because children often learn the English language more quickly than adults, their parents frequently use them as interpreters. I have seen children in the hospital or at a doctor's appointment when they should have been in school, because the parent needed them to interpret. Using children to interpret presents multiple problems. First, many issues are difficult for children to understand because of their immaturity. Second, there is no way to verify that what a child is saying is accurate or that they are telling the truth either to the parents or to the health care provider. And finally, children often have to miss school in order to interpret for their families. I remember having to interpret for my parents when I was very young. It forced me to grow up quickly and learn how to be responsible. However, I was lucky that my parents never asked me to interpret during a doctor's appointment or to explain certain issues that would be uncomfortable for a child.

Patients with language barriers will often go many, many years without seeking health care, and will avoid yearly physicals and screenings due to communication issues. Minorities with language barriers may not seek care until a situation becomes urgent or critical, leading them to overuse emergency rooms.

Language barriers create risks for miscommunications. For example, the English phrase "once a day" can be misinterpreted by a Spanish speaker as "eleven" since the Spanish word for eleven is *once*. It is important for local pharmacies to have information available in any languages used locally, in order to avoid unsafe use of medications. I have encountered many patients after their symptoms have not improved. When I ask if they took all of their medications, they usually say "no," because they could not understand the instructions given upon discharge from the hospital or the emergency room, or they did not understand the instructions on the pill bottle. Information about treatments or illnesses should be available in different languages, written at a sixth grade level for ease of understanding.

Language barriers may also limit the services available to non-English speakers. For example, psychiatric care may not be as readily available for those who do not speak English. But psychiatric care is important for those who have encountered atrocities associated with war or other difficulties in their homelands. Depression, panic disorders, and post-traumatic stress are common problems among these people.

> Minorities with language barriers may not seek care until a situation becomes urgent or critical, leading them to overuse emergency rooms.

Bridging the Language Gap— What Can You Do?

You may not have the answers or speak a different language, but you can learn what is available in your community for minorities. Many local hospitals offer Spanish for the health-care provider. If it is available to you, take advantage of it. Typically, these courses go through different levels—you can take one level and begin putting it into practice. Find out if your facility has employees who speak a language other than English. Call your social worker or manager and see if they can assist you in finding someone who can communicate with your immigrant or refugee patients. Many local hospitals also have telephone services that offer up to 150 languages via the telephone. Even though it is better to have an interpreter physically present, a phone conference can provide you with a trained interpreter who can ask questions and interpret necessary patient education. It may take some time and effort to assure that appropriate translators are available, but the improvement in patient care is worth it. I am a Spanish-speaking Nurse Practitioner; many patients who initially had to pay for an interpreter are now able to come to me without the worry of being turned away or having to pay money that could have been used for something else.

> *When people do not understand how health care services operate, or if they feel the providers do not understand their cultural needs, they may stay away out of fear and mistrust.*

Several textbooks are available to help you if you work in an area where a different language is needed. Spanish is the prevalent minority language in this country and therefore the Spanish resources available far surpass any other language. Books such as *Pocket Medical Spanish* (Dollinger 1992) can provide you with many different phrases (and phonetics) to get by until a trained interpreter becomes available. If you want to learn about different cultures, books such as *Culture and Nursing Care: A Pocket Guide* (Lipson, Dibble, and Minarik 1996) provide some useful tips on people of other cultures.

Look to see what documents have been translated in your place of employment. Is patient education available in another language? Have consents been translated? If not, talk to your supervisor about getting some key pieces translated into other languages. This is not only for the good of your client but also to protect you and your organization. Along with form translation, look for signage that needs to be displayed in other languages. You may need to work with leaders from particular people groups in your community to develop appropriate resources.

If you work in a hospital or clinic, it is not feasible to have translations of every language that you encounter. Typically, a facility must start providing forms in a particular language when 5% of the local population speaks that language. But the sooner you advocate for appropriate translation and interpretation services, the better, for safe, quality care and good customer service.

Fear or Access?

Many moderate- and larger-sized cities provide clinics that are either free or are affordable for those who are uninsured. Social work agencies, food banks, townships, and churches provide a variety of services, yet many people who need these services do not utilize them. Are the services underused because of problems with access, fear, or lack of understanding?

The Burmese refugees in Allen County, for example, have presented health care workers with some unusual problems. Their war-torn country has suffered great losses under the military dictatorship in power since 1962. In the World Health Report 2000, Burma ranked close to last in terms of overall health system performance; only Iraq and Syria ranked worst. Only the very rich and the military have had access to health care; the majority of the people have never been to a health care provider (Deleskey 1999). Like many other foreign-born people, they have only used and believed in folk medicine. Western medicine is strange and frightening to them.

Going to a gynecologist or getting

"screenings" is a completely new concept for these refugees. Their view of health is subjective, based only on how they are feeling. What is not felt is not threatening. They have never heard of diseases such as diabetes, hypertension, or high cholesterol. Even though many health fairs with free screenings target minorities, many will not go because they do not feel ill. If they did submit to a screening, having an abnormal blood test would not necessarily change their lifestyle habits.

When people do not understand how health care services operate, or if they feel the providers do not understand their cultural needs, they may stay away out of fear and mistrust. Once people from other cultures have lived here for many years, their exposure to our health care system increases and a certain trust begins to develop. However, if they remain poor and/or uninsured, they may still face issues of access similar to those of other poor minority groups.

As noted above, language and other cultural barriers prevent many people from knowing where health services can be obtained. I have participated in many health fairs as a volunteer interpreter. Even when the organizers have prepared and recruited interpreters, many of the people who need the services do not attend. Lack of attendance is often a marketing issue. The target population has to know the health fair is available. Questions to ask when planning an event include: Are informational flyers available in appropriate languages? Is the health fair publicized in newspapers that the targeted minorities read? Are local churches or temples assisting with the publicity?

The second issue associated with access is the location of services and health fairs in relation to public transportation. People of lower income may have to rely on public transportation or walk. Larger cities typically have comprehensive public transportation at relatively low cost. In smaller communities, however, bus routes may be very limited and the distance may be too great to travel on foot. Walking may also be dangerous in high-risk neighborhoods or where there are no sidewalks. People who rely on friends or relatives to give them rides often miss appointments when their rides do not show up. In my community, people of lower income tend to live on the south side of the city. Services in that community are disappearing—grocery stores, shopping centers, and physicians' offices are closing down and moving to other parts of the city. This limits that community's access to those services. There are a few physicians' offices on the south side, but their clientele base is large because these doctors are more in tune with the financial and cultural needs of their minority patients.

Location of services may be an issue in large or small cities. Bigger cities may have more accessible downtown hospitals and clinics, but hospitals and social agencies may build and expand on the outskirts of the city. In my area, for instance, our hospice services used to be located downtown, where it was accessible for the majority of the community. It relocated on the southwest side of the city, where it is less accessi-

> ### Drug Costs Comparisons
> • *Insulin: Lantus insulin (long acting) is $57.56 for 1000 units compared to $29.85 for Novolin NPH (long acting).*
> • *Antibiotics: Zithromax, six tablets of 250 mg. is $45.35 compared to $13.99 for six tablets of Doxycycline. Both are used to treat similar infections, such as chlamydia.*
> • *Antihypertensive: Lopressor, 60 tablets of 50mg. is $56.83 compared to generic Metoprolol for $7.99.*

ble to minority groups. The new location is beautiful but not convenient for many people. In another example, two brand new hospitals opened across the street from each other on the northeast side of our town, far from the reach of many minority groups. As an interpreter, I often get called to assist patients who ended up at the wrong hospital or who missed appointments because they couldn't find the right location.

> By recognizing that diversity exists in our communities, we can begin to resolve problems of language, access, and fear.

Financial issues often create insurmountable barriers to health care access among minority groups. Uninsured people may access care through the emergency room, but this alternative is expensive and lacks continuity of care. Or, as is often the case, health care providers simply do not consider the cost constraints poor people face, and fail to seek workable alternatives.

Opening Doors—What Can You Do?

A key to increasing access for minority patients is to consider ease of access when planning services and health fairs. Know what services are and are not available near your patient, and help work out a means of access. Advocate for services that are more conveniently located for the majority of minority patients.

You can also speak to your social workers or case managers to see what options are available if patients do not have health insurance, if they do not speak English, and/or if they are unable to get additional care after discharge. When I was a bedside nurse, I rarely knew my patient's financial status or whether he or she had insurance. As patient advocates we should be aware of these situations to bring them to the atten-

tion of physicians when they are prescribing certain medications or ordering different tests. Less-costly alternatives may be found with a little research and creativity.

Learn what the community agencies have to offer—is there medication or food assistance? Township offices may offer assistance with utility bills or even medication assistance. In the state of Indiana, for example, insulin is considered a life-saving drug and therefore no patient should be denied access to have insulin. Physicians or nurse practitioners can fill out insulin application forms that provide the patient with one-month supply of syringes, insulin vials, and blood sugar test strips. The patients can then go to a local pharmacy and receive insulin and other diabetes supplies to get them by until they can be seen at a local community clinic. You can also advocate for policy changes or seek funding to provide for the special needs of minority groups through foundations, grant sources, or other organizations that may consider funding creative ways to remove health care disparities.

By recognizing that diversity exists in our communities and identifying the cultural issues that need to be addressed, we can begin to resolve problems of language, access, and fear that might otherwise continue to cause disparity in health care provision. As we advocate for minority health care and seek out creative solutions, every effort counts and every piece of information becomes a powerful tool in working towards quality and safe care for every member of our communities.

QUESTIONS FOR DISCUSSION

1. Identify the minority groups (non-Anglo) in your own community, and share any unique care needs you know about for these groups.

2. Describe an experience you have had (positive or negative) related to minority health care.

3. How would you rate the accessibility to health care for minority groups in your community? Describe any barriers you are aware of that are related to fear or lack of understanding.

4. Complete the following sentence: One change I would like to make, to improve the health care of minority groups is....

SCENARIOS FOR LEARNING AND GROWTH

Read through the following scenarios and discuss the questions that follow them with the members of your group.

SCENARIO ONE: KETZY'S STORY

Ketzy was a bright 15-year-old. Even though she had only lived in the United States with her mother and sister for four years, she had mastered the English language and was excelling in school. She ran for student council and became a cheerleader in addition to earning A's and B's in her courses. Then her mother had a terrible car accident and ended up breaking both legs, two ribs, and one arm, and needed someone to assist in caring for her at home. Ketzy's mother did not speak any English and it was difficult to communicate with her during therapy sessions. Ketzy spent four days straight in the hospital—she wouldn't leave and her mother wouldn't let her leave. Ketzy was forced to leave school to provide care for her mother in the hospital and later at home. Her mother did not have any insurance and was here illegally.

1. What are the problems for the family in this scenario?

2. What are the problems for the health care providers in this scenario?

3. What options are available?

4. What could be done to prevent a situation like this from happening in the future?

5. What did you learn from this scenario and how might you apply it in your work?

SCENARIO TWO: LUPE'S DIABETES CLASS

A nurse practitioner receives a referral to consult with a woman, Lupe, who has gestational diabetes and needs insulin and an appropriate diet to prevent complications. Lupe attends the first session with her three small children but says that she is in a hurry because she is paying her driver $20 per hour and she can't afford to stay long. Her blood sugar is high during the session nd she needs to return in order to complete the diet education. The nurse practitioner schedules another appointment, but Lupe fails to show up for it. The nurse practitioner calls Lupe to find out how she is doing and why she has missed her appointment. Lupe tells the nurse that she had to choose between paying a driver to take her to the appointment or feeding her children, and he chose to feed her children.

1. What are the problems for the patient in this scenario?

2. What are the problems for the health care providers in this scenario?

3. What options are available?

4. What could be done to prevent a situation like this one from happening in the future?

5. What have you learned from this scenario and how might you apply it to your work?

REFERENCES

Abbott, P. D., E. Short, S. Dodson, C. Garcia, J. Perkins, and S. Wyant. 2002. Improving your cultural awareness with cultural clues. *The Nurse Practitioner* 27 (2): 44-51.

American Public Health Association. 2005. Minority health links. http://www.apha.org/public_health/minority.htm.

Betancourt, J. R., A. G. Green, and J. E. Carillo. 2002. Cultural competence in health care: Emerging frameworks and practical approaches. Quality of Care for Underserved Populations. The Commonwealth Fund: Field Report.

Burma Project. n.d. Ethnic groups. http://www.burmaproject.org/CRISIS/ethnic.html.

Burrows N. R., J. Lojo, M. M. Engelgau, and L. S. Geiss. 2004. Using survey data for diabetes surveillance among minority populations: a report of the Centers for Disease Control and Prevention's expert panel meeting. *Prev Chronic Dis* [serial online], April. http://www.cdc.gov/pcd/issues/2004/apr/03_0018.htm.

CDC. 2004. Health disparities experienced by racial/ethnic minority populations. MMWR Weekly, August 27, 2004. http://www.cdc.gov/mmwr/preview/mmwrhtml/mm5333a1.htm.

CDC. 2005. Hispanic or Latino populations. Office of Minority Health. http://www.cdc.gov/omh/Populations/HL/hl.htm.

Chin, J. L. 2000. Culturally competent health care. *Public Health Reports* 115: 25-33.

Deleskey, K. 1999. Health care in Burma. *JONA* 29 (10): 41-48.

Dollinger, R. K. 1992. *Pocket Medical Spanish: An instant self-use interpreting aid for medical professionals.* Reseda, CA: JVD Publishing Company.

Idrogo, M., and R. Mazze. 2004. Diabetes in the Hispanic population: High risk warrants targeted screening and treatment. *Postgraduate Medicine* 116 (6): 26-36.

Leininger, M. M. 1991. *Culture Care Diversity & Universality: A Theory of Nursing.* New York: National League for Nursing Press.

Lipson, J. G., S. L. Dibble, and P. A. Minarik. 1996. *Culture and Nursing Care: A Pocket Guide.* San Francisco: University of California San Francisco Nursing Press.

Rasbridge, L. A. n.d. Background on refugees: Refugee definition and process. http://www3.baylor.edu/~Charles_Kemp/background_on_refugees.htm.

Poverty and Health in Developing Countries: The Case of Peru and Bolivia

by Dan Clark

Summary: Poverty and poor health form a vicious cycle, particularly in developing countries where overall resources are scarce and indigenous and cultural differences influence the causes of illness and its treatment. Clark analyzes international causes of poverty and poor health then presents a number of creative initiatives in Bolivia and Peru that aim to improve the lives of the poor within these countries. Cultural and spiritual facets of poverty are also considered.

Walter and Maria are an Aymara Indian couple living in La Paz, Bolivia. Maria is pregnant. A male midwife attends Maria when the baby is born. He immediately wraps up the baby in clothes and tells Maria the baby needs to go to the hospital. Walter and Maria do not take the baby to the hospital and the newborn baby dies. Why did this baby die? From parental neglect? From ignorance? From cultural beliefs about newborns? Because Walter and Maria do not have money to pay for treatment for the baby? As God's punishment because Maria got pregnant before they got married, when they knew as Christians they should wait? What if

the reasons for the baby's death persist; what then are the prospects for the health and longevity of any future children Walter and Maria may have?

High infant mortality rates are just one of the health problems in developing countries. Complex explanations lie behind the statistical "numbers" used to define illness, poverty, and mortality in public health data worldwide. Poverty is no stranger to humanity. Worldwide over one billion people, or roughly four times the population of the United States, live in poverty. A significant percentage of the world's population will live its whole life in poverty.

This article addresses the relationship between poverty and health in developing countries, particularly in Peru and Bolivia. We want to look briefly at what characterizes poverty, and what the relationship is between poverty and health. We will outline some possible causes of poverty in developing countries. We will present approaches that attempt to improve the situation of the poor. Finally, we will examine a key role and

> We need not feel overwhelmed about the impact we can make compared to the need. The danger is in doing nothing, for in doing nothing both the poor and we are the losers. There is room for pioneers, for the bold, for those who will be different. For Christian health professionals, the challenge and the call are not only to discharge duties honorably, but The poor will most likely become worse off if the focus of these debates is on cost containment and overuse of health care rather than prevention and the needs of the poor. To honor God and serve others...that is the way to make a difference to the whole person.

Dan Clark earned a Ph.D. in Pharmacology before serving 15 years with his family as missionaries in Peru and Bolivia. He currently resides in Indiana and conducts research at Indiana University School of Medicine. He is fluent in Spanish.

challenge for Christian health professionals.

Who Are The Poor?

Poverty can be defined in different ways, based on the criteria used. Internationally, families who fall below the "Poverty Line" lack the income necessary to purchase "a basic basket of goods and services fulfilling basic food and non-food needs" (Republic of Bolivia 2001, 21). According to this indicator, in 2001-2002, 55% of the homes in Peru and 64% in Bolivia were poor. The number living in extreme poverty was 24% and 37%, in Peru and Bolivia, respectively (Kim et al. 2000; INEI n.d., INEI 2002).

While the Poverty Line focuses on income, poverty is multidimensional. The human deprivation of poverty is reflected at the individual, societal, and international levels: economic (income, livelihoods, decent work), human (health, education), political (empowerment, rights, voice), socio-cultural (status, dignity) and protective (insecurity, risk, vulnerability) (INEI 2002; WHO 2003; Bowyer 2004).

The populations of Peru and Bolivia illustrate the heterogeneous character of poverty. Half of the poor live in urban marginal areas while the other half is rural. Political and economic deprivation and geographic isolation are significant factors for the rural poor, whereas the primary deprivation of the urban poor is economic. The multifaceted, typically intergenerational nature of rural poverty in developing countries is called endemic poverty. Nearly 10% of the population of Peru lives in endemic poverty (INEI 2002; INEI n.d.; Republic of Bolivia 2001).

Getting caught up in the "numbers" of health and need is easy. It is important, however, to realize that real persons in need lie behind the statistics.

We will now look at the relationship between poverty and health.

How Poverty Affects Health In A Developing Country

Poverty and poor health form a vicious cycle. Poor health can result simply from economic deficits in which limited resources force families to make decisions about health care. In Bolivia, if a choice must be made between going to the doctor for a problem of coughing up thick yellow sputum nocturnally (a chronic symptom of tuberculosis) and paying the children's school bill (an acute financial need), the parent may well choose to pay the school bill, at the expense of his or her health.

Families with scarce nutritional resources may distribute food in ways that compromise the health of some family members to preserve the health of others. In the Peruvian highlands, working men and income-earning children often receive more and better food than infants and women. Living in perpetual economic crisis, these families save their limited resources to get treatment for only the most serious illnesses, while they ignore lesser health problems. When medical expenses are unavoidable, these families spend most of their money on transportation and medical attention, leaving them little or nothing with which to pay for medicines and other supplies. Paying for health care may mean not eating certain meals or eating only on certain days. The resulting compromised health leads to poor work and economic deprivation; and so turns the cycle of poverty (Graham 1997; Oths 1994; Cotlear 2000).

> The human deprivation of poverty is reflected at the individual, societal, and international levels: economic, human, political, socio-cultural, and protective.

Apart from income, a variety of factors influences the health of the poor: age, sex, genetic heredity, educational level, food security, environmental conditions (polluted air, sound pollution, security, housing), access to water and sanitation, and access to adequate health care. Government economic policies also affect household income and nutritional status, as well as health care (WHO 2003).

Social and psychological factors also impact health. Families in poverty in Bolivia live in a context of malnutrition and lack of basic health and social care. Some parents may be so occupied with work and the worries of life that their children are deprived of the resources that will ensure a healthy outcome when illness arises (Sevilla et al. 2000).

> Health and poverty are international concerns, not just personal or national ones.

Indigenous and cultural differences influence the health of the poor. Many indigenous groups have a unique understanding of the cause of illness and its treatment. They may or may not readily accept the ideas of modern medicine. In Peru and Bolivia, the geographic isolation of many indigenous groups hampers the government's attempts to provide improved health care for all (Junge 1994).

Even disease patterns vary across social class. The pattern of diseases prevalent among the global poor differs from that of the population of the world as a whole. Communicable diseases are heavily concentrated among the poor. The Peruvian Ministry of Health reported that communicable diseases are responsible for 45% of deaths among the poorest 20% of the population, while responsible for only 22% of deaths among the richest 20% (Gwatkin and Guillot 2000). Noncommunicable diseases also cause excess death and disability among the poor. Thus, death and disability rates from both noncommunicable and communicable diseases are higher for the poor than for the rich (Gwatkin and Guillot, 2000).

If so many people live in poverty, and poverty affects health, how do people become poor and what keeps them in poverty or in poor health? Can health be improved without dealing with poverty?

Causes Of Poor Health And Poverty

Poverty and poor health point to inequalities; some have enough or more than enough resources to sustain life adequately while others do not. We have seen that personal and social factors contribute significantly to poverty. Lack of education, poor choices, and the home environment affect a person's well being.

Health and poverty are international concerns, not just personal or national ones. Organizations such as the World Health Organization (WHO), the World Bank, and the International Monetary Fund (IMF) are major players in international health and economics. One weakness at this international level is inadequate targeting and defining of the poor. Estimates of the global burden of disease are based on the total world population, whereas around 24 percent of the world's population is classified as poor. Therefore, policies and programs based on global data may not effectively impact the poor. Much public health information is based on mortality and incidence of disease data. This gives little perspective on the cause or time course of disease. Some experts now recommend a "life course approach" whereby influences on health across a lifetime are used to give information for attacking poverty and poor health (Gwatkin and Guillot 2000; Leon and Gill 2001).

Inadequate targeting of the poor also occurs when government subsidies are diverted to the non-poor. A study in Peru showed that around half of the exemptions and reduced rates for health care actually reached the richer 60% of households (Cotlear 2000; Leon and Gill 2001).

Poor use of public funding and corruption impedes the improvement of health and income for the poor. *El Comercio*, a major newspaper in Lima, Peru, reported in 2003 that inadequate administration of projects intended to alleviate poverty for the poor resulted in a loss of the equivalent of 80 million dollars (*El Comercio* 2005).

On the international level, the predominant thinking for many years has been that if poverty and poor health are interrelated, then alleviating poverty should improve health. From this perspective, decisions makers concluded that economic progress is the real key to enhancing health and reducing poverty. To achieve economic progress, the World Band and the IMF have promoted the practice of financial structural adjustment to the governments of developing countries. To receive loans, poor countries are forced to increase their integration in and dependence upon the global market economy, even though they may not be in a position to effectively compete in that market. The international debt obligations from this restructuring have forced poor countries to put debt repayment ahead of domestic priorities, such as health and poverty. In the rush to pay debts and be competitive, attending to the poor is often relegated to a secondary level (Leon and Gill 2001; Kim et al. 2000).

When Alberto Fujimori became President of Peru, he initiated a government finance structural adjustment. Under pressure from creditors and aid agencies, in 1997 the Peruvian government adjusted the national health care financing strategy. Moving away from direct central government involvement in the provision of health care services, the government guaranteed the right to unrestricted access to services (anyone could sign up), but no guarantee on how the poor would pay for services. Thus, many Peruvians were left without

health care (Kim et al. 2000).

The global health of the poor is also influenced by transnational corporations (TNCs). At the end of the 1970s, many nations could not pay their foreign debt. The structural adjustment policy advocated by the IMF and the World Bank produced a cash deficit for many poorer nations. In the urgency to compete in the global market economy and increase their cash resources, nations offered incentives to attract TNCs. The presence of TNCs in developing countries has brought jobs, income, and new technologies.

On the downside, the offers by poor countries to TNCs may assume the use of child labor, lower health and safety standards, and sweatshop working conditions. Nations may also allow permissive environmental laws to encourage investment. This has led to significant ecological degradation: deforestation, oil spills, and poisoned waterways (Kim et al. 2000).[1]

Non-government organizations (NGOs), such as Food for the Hungry, and Doctors Without Borders, among many others, have been viewed as key players in health care and development for the poor. At times, they have been caught in the middle. On one side, the World Bank and other international organizations have relied on NGOs as facilitators of funding and administration for their own programs. This can limit the NGOs' independence and ability to carry out their own goals. On the other side, when national governments, such as Peru's, have cut social programs,

> Poor use of public funding and corruption impedes the improvement of health and income for the poor.

they have hoped NGOs would fill in the gaps of social need. Critics consider this to be an abandonment of the government's social responsibility, detrimental to the poor. The NGOs have neither the resources nor scope of action to take on such roles effectively (Kim et al. 2000).

The influences on the health of the poor in developing countries are many and complex; the answers need to be equal to the task. In the next section, we will examine some ways this problem has been addressed in Peru and Bolivia.

Responses To The Need

To address the tremendous needs in the areas of poverty and health care, the international public health community has advocated a "pro-poor health approach." This emphasis gives priority to promoting, protecting, and improving the health of the poor. Public health leaders realize that a "one-size-fits-all" answer will not work in every context. The task is so large and complex that people at all levels, from international to local, must be involved.

> To work in alleviating poverty and poor health in developing countries, one must have short-term goals while maintaining a long-term perspective.

As a pro-poor response, the WHO created a Division of Intensified Cooperation with Countries and Peoples in Greatest Need. This initiative is country-specific, recognizing that a country's health development is rooted in a historical, cultural, political, and socioeconomic context. The initiative is multisectoral, recognizing that solutions to poverty and health must involve development initiatives as well as health sector changes.

In implementation of its initiative, the WHO supported a social security health plan developed by the Tupiza Province Secretariat of Bolivia. Funds from various sources provided health care for the poorest people of the province. This health project in one province has provided a model for the whole country of Bolivia (Jancloes 1998).

Government-sponsored programs present promise for better health care for the poor. In 2001, the Peruvian government launched the Integral Health Insurance program (Seguro Integral de Salud, or SIS). The pro-poor design of this plan offers varying levels of coverage to different segments of the population in poverty. The SIS program may provide access to health care that has been beyond the reach of the poorest Peruvians (SIS n.d.; Bolivia Ministry n.d.).

One of the difficulties to providing health care to the rural poor is distance and isolation. The Peruvian government and an NGO have collaborated in a telemedicine project that can potentially alleviate the problem of distance between health care recipient and health professional. The EHAS project (Spanish acronym for Hispanic American Health Link) encompasses two major river networks in the Peruvian jungle, the Marañón and Huallaga rivers. A radio transmitter links jungle health posts with a major university in Lima. Rural health workers consult by email and voice mail on medical situations in the jungle. Before this project existed, the average number of consults was three per month per clinic. With the new technology, the number of consultations rose to 23 per month per facility (Martinez et al. 2003).

Many public health experts understand that economic development, in itself, is not the ultimate answer to poverty and well being. Economic development must be directed specifically toward improving the lives of the poor; in other words, improved income for a country does not guarantee a better life for the poor. To be most effective, projects must be well-designed and managed, as well as targeted specifically to the poor.

The Andean Rural Health Care (AHRC) program is an NGO that functions in the Bolivian highlands among the Aymara and Quechua Indians. It relies on the household census and epidemiological data to determine its strategies and impact. The AHRC works intimately with the community, so its success depends heavily on trust. The many activities of the program are subservient to its goal: to improve the status of the poor, as measured by a reduction in morbidity and mortality (Perry et al. 1999).

In an urban context, a tuberculosis project in Carabayllo, a poor neighborhood of Lima, Peru, is a model for the successful treatment of multidrug resistant tuberculosis. Partners in Health, an NGO based in Boston, in conjunction with its sister organization in Lima, Socios en Salud, achieved a cure rate of at least 80% in Carabayllo for this form of tuberculosis, previously thought untreatable in a resource-poor setting. Encouraged by these results, the Peruvian Ministry of Health, Partners in Health, and the Institute for Healthcare Improvement combined forces to raise the cure-rate and to expand to include a larger segment of the poor neighborhoods of Lima. The success of two NGOs stimulated the government to get involved (Berwick 2004).

Health care professionals and development experts alone cannot reduce poverty and improve health. Local communities and individuals must be recruited, empowered, and involved in solving their needs. This may involve education. It may necessitate new government approaches and policies. Many who have worked in community development and poverty have learned that for progress to be made, those in need must desire a better life and be willing to expend effort to attain it. If the desire and effort is lacking, when a program runs short of resources or the experts leave, the people usually return to their previous habits and end up as before (Leon and Gill 2001).

Governments understand this human tendency. They have developed initiatives to work with communities at their points of need. In Peru, the Local Health Administration Committee (CLAS) program gives authority and autonomy to local communities in administering health care. Since many of the workers in the CLAS clinics are people of the community, there is a higher trust level and better results than with traditional government-sponsored clinics. However, no solution is universally successful. The CLAS function best in some settings, and less well in others (Bowyer 2004).

International agencies and national governments know that not all aspects of inadequate health care and poverty will ever fully be addressed. They tend to work with global and national data that can omit or insufficiently measure human need. We do well to remember that despite the good intentions of these organizations, intractable problems will remain.

Personal and cultural factors will always hinder development efforts. Imagine the point of view of indigenous peoples, who are often some of the poorest and most difficult to impact. If indigenous groups prefer to keep their traditional lifestyles and geographic location, how much should the government intervene to improve life for them? Some individuals and people groups will not want to be incorporated into government programs, if it means significant change for them. If they are accustomed to a subsistence lifestyle, should they be forced to integrate into the modern global market? If they are accustomed to a certain level of health and care that is acceptable to them, is it necessary to provide more, even if the morbidity and mortality rates are above international and national levels?

> Many who have worked in community development and poverty have learned that for progress to be made, those in need must desire a better life and be willing to expend effort to attain it.

Often, the impact on indigenous groups depends upon change among the leaders or among the few who like innovation. Hector Canqui is an Aymara Indian who lives with his family on the altiplano of Bolivia. His brother received training in agriculture through the organization Food For The Hungry. They obtained the materials to build a large greenhouse that provides vegetables and fruit for their families. By having a steady supply of nutrient-rich food, their children are healthier than neighboring children whose families do not have greenhouses.

We may draw two conclusions from this example. First, those who accept change may significantly influence those who are more resistant to change. Hector's neighbors will want a greenhouse so their children will have less illness too. Second, there must be a balance between modernization and indigenous values. Hector and his family did not completely alter their lifestyle, but they were willing to make changes to have better health.

> *Whatever the reasons for poverty, its resolution includes an inner, spiritual transformation.*

To work in alleviating poverty and poor health in developing countries, we must have short-term goals while maintaining a long-term perspective. We want to help people have a better life now, but the human tendency to resist change frequently stymies that goal. Thus, we will do well to realize that efforts today will primarily bring positive effects for the young and for future generations, more than for current adults.

Filling In The Gap

After looking at issues of health and poverty in developing countries from a socioeconomic perspective, we will now turn to a more basic issue. Why should anyone care about the health of the poor? It could be for humanitarian concerns. Some persons do become involved for these reasons, in order to make a difference. But why would the rich care enough to give up their hard-earned resources to help people they do not know? It seems unlikely that the world's leaders or a significant number of influential people will change their philosophy from a materialistic, economic, and power-based one to a singular focus in trying to bring more equity worldwide, in health and well being. This may seem pessimistic, but it scratches at the surface of something deeper.

The glaring gap in development and international public health literature is the spiritual dimension of humanity. Today, medical care in the United States recognizes the importance of the spiritual aspect to effective healing. It seems logical that the same would be true for other areas of human existence, as well. Jesus said, "I have come that they might have life, and have it to the full" (John 10:10, NIV). Concern for health and well being encompasses all facets of human existence, including the spiritual facet.

Christians believe all humans are created in God's image and that we must not be indifferent to the suffering of others, because they are equal with us before the Creator. The Old Testament makes very clear God's concern that his people take care of the poor, the needy, and the suffering. A number of laws about land distribution in Israel, especially regarding the prohibition on selling ancestral land and the time limitations on voluntary slavery, have a basis in preventing extreme need among the Israelites.

Whatever the reasons for poverty, its resolution includes an inner, spiritual transformation; the most fundamental issue of poverty is humanity's separation from God. External transformation does not deal with the whole problem of poverty. Man must change from his basic selfishness and materialism to a dependence on God and a true concern for others. That is the true basis of the solution to poverty. It is equally valid for the economically disadvantaged and for those who would help the poor.

Amidst the struggles of the poor in developing countries there are lights of hope. Holistic ministries carried out principally by Christian groups seek to impact people in whatever area of need they may have. They fill in the gap left open by other workers in health and poverty by addressing unreached dimensions of human need.

It is not just North American and European Christians who work to improve the lot of the poor in developing countries. In the midst of their own challenges, Christians in countries like Peru and Bolivia also strive to help others.

In response to the unmet need they see every day, the professionals of a Christian denomination in Peru organized a national organization called APRONAP (Association of Nazarene Professionals of Peru). Their desire was to use their expertise, leadership skills, and influence to help the less fortunate. Registered with the government as an NGO, APRONAP's impact has been felt in Lima, the capital. Health professionals in a local church hold clinics in their church building, as well as in poorer areas of Lima. They provide free health screening and teaching, with an eye to the deeper needs of those to whom they minister.

During the last major episode of the El Niño phenomenon in Peru, a pastor challenged his congregation, "If you have five shirts in your closet, give three. If you have three shirts, give two. There are others affected by El Niño who are in greater need." Many churches collected food, clothing, and other goods that were shipped to areas of Peru greatly affected by El Niño.

Recently, Nelson Mandela said, "The world is hungry for action, not words. In this new century, millions of people in the world's poorest countries remain…trapped in the prison of poverty. It is time to set them free…there is a unique opportunity for making an impact" (CNN 2005).

Amidst the struggles of the poor in developing countries there are lights of hope.

We need not feel overwhelmed about the impact we can make compared to the need. The danger is in doing nothing, for in doing nothing both the poor and we are the losers. There is room for pioneers, for the bold, for those who will be different. For Christian health professionals, the challenge and the call are not only to discharge duties honorably, but to honor God and serve others. That is the way to make a difference to the whole person.

NOTES

1. See the *Mountain Voices*, the Oral Testimony Programme of the Panos Institute, for enlightening information on the environmental and lifestyle impact of mining by TNCs in the Peruvian highlands. http://www.mountainvoices.org/intro.html

QUESTIONS FOR DISCUSSION

1. How do poverty and poor health differ in developing nations compared to the U.S.?

2. If you are familiar with the culture and/or conditions in a particular developing nation, share what you know with your group.

3. What are some of the non-health issues in developing countries that affect the poor? How should we, as Americans, respond to these issues?

4. Consider the creative initiatives from Bolivia and Peru presented by the author. Which ones do you think will be the most effective?

5. The author raises the following questions. How would you respond?

   "If indigenous groups prefer to keep their traditional lifestyle and geographic location, how much should the government intervene to improve life for them?"

   "Some individuals and people groups will not want to be incorporated into government programs, if it means significant change for them. If they are accustomed to a subsistence lifestyle, should they be forced to integrate into the modern global market?

   "If they are accustomed to a certain level of health and care that is acceptable to them, is it necessary to provide more, even if the morbidity and mortality rates are above international and national levels?

6. Do you agree or disagree that "spiritual transformation" needs to be an integral part of resolving issues of poverty? Why do you feel this way?

REFERENCES

Berwick, D. M. 2004. Lessons from developing nations on improving health care. *British Medical Journal* 328:1124-1129.

Bolivia Ministry of Health and Social Provision (Ministerio de Salud y Previsión Social Bolivia). n.d. http://www.sns.gov.bo/.

Bowyer, T. 2004. Popular participation and the state: democratizing the health sector in rural Peru. *International Journal of Health Planning and Management* 19 (2): 131-61.

CNN.Com. 2005. Mandela: Rich must feed the poor. February 3, 2005. http://www.cnn.com/2005/WORLD/europe/02/03/mandela.london/index.html.

Cotlear, D. 2000. Peru: Reforming health care for the poor. *The World Bank LCSHD Paper Series*, no. 57.

El Comercio (Lima, Peru). 2005. Perú perdió S/. 266 millones por mal gasto social en 2003. January 12, 2005. http://www.elcomercioperu.com.pe/online/.

Graham, M. A. 1997. Food allocation in rural Peruvian households: Concepts and behavior regarding children. *Social Science and Medicine* 11:1697 1709.

Gwatkin, D. R., and M. Guillot. 2000. *The burden of disease among the global poor.* Washington, D.C.: The World Bank.

Instituto Nacional de Estadística e Informática (INEI). n.d. Bolivia: Indicadores de Pobreza Moderada Por Año Según Área Geográfica, 1999-2002. http://www.ine.gov.bo/.

Instituto Nacional de Estadística e Informática (INEI). 2002. Condiciones de Vida en los Departamentos del Perú, 2001. Lima, Peru. http://www.inei.gob.pe/PeruCifrasITM/banner/documentos/CondicionesDepartamental.pdf.

Jancloes, M. 1998. The poorest first: WHO's activities to help the people in greatest need. *World Health Forum* 19 (2): 182-187.

Junge B. 1994. Indigenous concepts useful in programs. Experiences in the Bolivian highlands. *Sante Salud* 10 (Spring): 1.

Kim J. Y., J. V. Millen, A. Irwin, and J. Gershman, eds. 2000. *Dying for growth: Global inequality and the health of the poor.* Monroe, ME: Common Courage Press, and Cambridge, MA: The Institute for Health and Social Justice, Partners in Health.

Leon, D., and W. Gill, eds. 2001. *Poverty, inequality, and health.* New York: Oxford University Press.

Martinez, A., V. Villarroel, J. Seoane, and F. J. del Pozo. 2003. A study of a rural telemedicine system in the Amazon region of Peru. *Telemed Telecare* 10 (4): 219-25.

Oths, K. S. 1994. Health care decisions of households in economic crisis: An example from the Peruvian highlands. *Human Organization* 53 (3): 245- .

Perry, H. et al. 1999. Attaining health for all through community partnerships: principles of the census-based, impact-oriented (CBIO) approach to primary health care developed in Bolivia, South America. *Social Science & Medicine* 48:1053-1067.

Sevilla, R. et al. 2000. "CLAPSEN," a global approach to the rehabilitation of severe childhood malnutrition in Bolivia. *Sante* 10 (2): 97-102.

Republic of Bolivia: Poverty Reduction Strategy Paper. 2001. Retrieved from IMF website: http://www.imf.org/external/NP/prsp/2001/bol/01/Index.htm.

Seguro Integral de Salud. (SIS). n.d. Ministerio de Salud, Peru (Integral Health Insurance). http://www.sis.minsa.gob.pe/.

World Health Organization (WHO). 2003. Poverty and health. Geneva: Organisation for Economic Co-operation and Development. http://whqlibdoc.who.int/publications/2003/9241562366.pdf.

Innovative Health Care Models for the Inner City Poor

by Janet Eddy

Summary: Successful long-term solutions to the challenges faced by inner city residents and health care providers will require attention to some significant barriers. Eddy describes some innovative inner city health care models and identifies keys to their success.

In America, the ability to enjoy good health is not an inalienable right. The inner city poor struggle for survival and have a complex set of challenges to their health. This article will discuss common medical problems of inner city residents and barriers to accessing care. Several programs with innovative approaches to inner city health care will be examined.

Major Health Issues

Between 1979 and 1994, the number of U.S. children under six years of age living in poverty increased from 3.5 to 6.1 million (Andrulis 1998). As of 2004, 23% of all U.S. children were considered impoverished. Inner city children living in poverty have higher than normal rates of asthma, lead toxicity, dental decay, obesity and Type II diabetes, and victimization by violence (Graham 2004; McMillan et al. 1999; Anderson 1999).

Lead toxicity among children, associated with exposure to lead-based paint, occurs most often in children who live in older homes. In the inner city, much of the affordable housing is in such homes. Young children may ingest peeling lead-based paint and children playing in yards where old houses have been razed are exposed to lead through the soil. The cost of lead abatement is high.

> The inner city poor struggle for survival and have a complex set of challenges to their health.

Adult residents of the inner city are also likely to suffer from higher than normal rates of asthma, obesity and Type II diabetes, and the effects of violence. Heart disease, hypertension, certain cancers, some substance abuse disorders, HIV, and Hepatitis C are prevalent (Freeman and Alshafie 2002; Newman et al. 2001; Wenzel et al. 2004; Nyamathi et al. 2002).

Although the etiology of asthma is multifactorial, urban populations have higher than average exposure to air pollutants, which have been implicated in causing and

Janet Eddy, M.D., is assistant professor in the Department of Family Medicine at Virginia Commonwealth University Health System in Richmond, VA and maintains a clinical practice at VCU's Nelson Clinic. Her clinical specialties are Family Practice and Underserved Populations. She has been the medical director of Craig Health Center since its inception in 1997. The Center provides comprehensive health care to impoverished people, including services for medical care, mental health, nutrition, and assistance with medications.

perpetuating asthma. Obesity and Type II diabetes, hypertension and heart disease are associated with high calorie diets and lack of exercise, although genetic factors are also involved. The poor diet of many inner city residents may result from poor dietary habits over generations, insufficient access to fresh fruits and vegetables because of cost, limited access to quality grocery stores, and easy fast food access. Lack of a safe place to exercise or facilities that encourage exercise contributes to a sedentary lifestyle that compounds these problems (Powell, Slater, and Chaloupka 2004).

> For the uninsured individual who is leading a day-to-day existence, health care is out of reach unless a major illness or injury occurs.

Higher cancer rates among inner city residents may be related to pollution and toxin exposure, lack of preventive care and screening, poor diet and other lifestyle issues. Substance abuse has wreaked havoc on the inner city, making its streets more dangerous, its families less stable, and intensifying poverty. Users of "crack" cocaine and heroin often engage in prostitution in exchange for drugs and are therefore at high risk for HIV infection, as are their sexual partners. In addition, Hepatitis C is prevalent among people who have injected drugs. Few people addicted to these drugs can escape poverty, violence, or poor health.

The prevalence of drugs and violence also has a profound effect on law-abiding residents of inner city neighborhoods, who often become victims of random violence, get caught in the middle of gang violence, and get robbed at gunpoint by addicts who are driven by their drug habit (Anderson 1999). Many inner city children have witnessed violent death in their neighborhoods. Too often, children are seduced into drug use by drug addicts or dealers in their own community.

Barriers To Health Care

The combined effects of poverty, low educational levels, and poor or absent primary medical care are barriers to early diagnosis and treatment of disease. Lack of insurance is the single largest barrier to obtaining health care (Andrulis 1998). For the uninsured individual who is leading a day-to-day existence with regard to food and shelter, health care is out of reach unless a major illness or injury occurs (Sung, Alema-Mensch, and Blumenthal 2002).

Language and culture are barriers for many people. The inner city is a melting pot of people from diverse cultural backgrounds, some of whom do not speak English, and who frequently have health habits and beliefs much different from those of western medicine. The non-citizen, especially the non-citizen who does not speak English, often has minimal access to care (Derose and Baker 2000).

Some African Americans and members of other minority groups are suspicious of traditional health care systems because of perceived past exploitation for research purposes (Blumenthal, Sung et al. 1995). In urban settings, there are a large number of disenfranchised people, including substance abusers and the mentally ill, who will not access health care unless desperate.

Challenges For Health Providers

Health care providers working with the inner city poor face significant challenges. Three of the most common challenges are noncompliance, crisis mode, and social situations.

Noncompliance

Impoverished persons have difficulty complying with medical care for a variety of reasons, including competing priorities, lack of finances, poor health habits that have been present throughout life, mental illness, difficulty understanding complex medical regimens, lack of social supports, and lack of transportation. Institutions and providers often accentuate barriers when they don't acknowledge the complex challenges of inner city poverty.

Health care workers at inner city clinics can respond to noncompliance in a positive way by scheduling "walk-in" times, allowing flexibility in the day's schedule, and by providing night and weekend hours. Noncompliance should be a clue to the provider to learn more about the patient's home life, level of stress and despondency, education and reading level, comprehension of his or her illness and treatment, and ability to purchase necessary supplies. The provider who asks about these issues will gain a better understanding of the situation and foster a therapeutic relationship that can enhance the patient's self-efficacy.

The Crisis Mode

As mentioned above, many people wait until their condition has seriously deteriorated before they approach the health care worker. With medical issues, this is dangerous, requires more resources, and tends to put the health care worker in crisis mode him/herself. Common examples of such "crises" are the patient with a very high glucose and dehydration, or the patient with very high blood pressure. The correct response to urgent problems like these, if one is not in an emergency room setting, is to get the patient to the emergency room. But suppose the client has young children with her or unattended at home? Suppose he refuses to go to the emergency room because he knows he can't pay the hospital bill or has to get to work? Clinicians who have worked in the third world are in familiar territory here. It is an uncomfortable position to be in, but it is the reality of life for the inner city poor and their doctors and nurses.

Social Situations

The majority of medical situations among the urban poor are inextricably linked with a social situation, and unless the health care worker can offer solutions for both, he or she is unlikely to be effective. The woman whose blood pressure is out of control is unlikely to get better unless one addresses the fact that she is overwhelmed trying to care for the three grandchildren who have recently come into her custody. The 16-year-old with chronic headaches probably won't respond to treatment until one addresses the fact that his family relies on him as the breadwinner and the translator. How can the child with a high lead level be treated when his mother can't afford to move the family or get the lead removed from the house? Physicians and nurses are generally not trained to address situations like these, which is why a multidisciplinary team is essential. Social workers, psychologists, psychiatrists, nutritionists, epidemiologists, pharmacists, dentists, and lawyers are some of the necessary team members when dealing with the needs of the poor. Since most health care settings have few of these professionals on site, the health care worker must be able to access help for the patient from outside agencies.

Systems To Increase Access To Care

Over the years, inner city residents have obtained health care in emergency rooms, often in desperation. This is a costly way to receive primary medical care, and prevention and screening are not available through the emergency room. Following are some of the options available to change this trend and help inner city residents receive more effective primary and preventive care.

Medicare and Medicaid

Medicaid is a state-administered program that provides medical care and medication to low-income children and their mothers, most disabled people, and impoverished nursing home residents. Medicaid eligibility for children expanded in the late 1980s to mid-1990s, which greatly improved access to health care among impoverished children. Unfortunately, the vast majority of impoverished adults are not eligible for Medicaid (McMillan et al. 1999).

Medicare is a federally administered insurance program that covers citizens 65 years of age and older. It provides a quality health care safety net for elderly individuals. Until 2004, Medicare didn't cover medication, but the program is phasing in a plan to help cover prescription medicine.

Other Resources

Other resources for obtaining health care include community health centers funded by the federal government, health departments, community mental health centers, and university clinics funded by the state, and privately funded clinics. Community health centers generally provide primary care, medication, and sometimes dental services on a sliding fee scale based on income in some designated health care shortage areas (Blumenthal, Mort, and Edwards 1995, 253-273). The federal government also funds clinics for homeless people in some cities.

Each state funds health departments in all cities and counties. Health departments provide preventive services like pap smears, contraception, and well baby care as well as screening and treatment for sexually transmitted diseases, and occasionally limited primary and dental care.

States are mandated to have community mental health centers in every city and county, providing psychiatric care to the mentally ill on a sliding fee scale. However, most of these centers have long waiting lists and many provide care only to those people with the most severe psychiatric diseases.

State-funded universities often provide primary, specialty, and inpatient care to uninsured people on a sliding fee scale based on income.

Localities and private foundations across the country fund free clinics and other health centers to care for underserved populations. These clinics generally are inadequately funded to provide care for the number of individuals who need their services.

Dental care is one of the biggest needs for the impoverished in our country, one that is seldom addressed by any of the above systems. Most impoverished people do not get dental care except in emergencies.

Models That Work

There are five key factors to a successful inner city health care model—it must provide quality medical care for free or for a reasonable income-based fee, offer services that are valued by the community served,

> **Five Key Factors To A Successful Inner City Health Care Model**
> - *Provide quality medical care for free or for a reasonable income-based fee*
> - *Offer services that are valued by the community it serves*
> - *Acknowledge the constraints of the population*
> - *Build on the strengths of the individuals it serves*
> - *Develop partnerships with other community resources*

acknowledge the constraints of the population, build on the strengths of the individuals served, and develop partnerships with other community resources. We will examine three successful models in Richmond, Virginia, a city of 500,000 with a large inner city population.

Comprehensive Primary Care

Community-based primary care programs for underserved populations are associated with lower rates of hospitalization and improved control over chronic illnesses. (Blumenthal, Mort, and Edwards 1995, 253-273). The Craig Health Center is a community-based program that provides comprehensive primary care to medically underserved adults and children. "At Craig, the average adult patient is on six medications, has three medical diagnoses, a full-time job, and no insurance," according to Judy Parker-Falzoi, the nurse practitioner and clinic director. The clinic was established in 1997 to provide acute and chronic disease management using a multidisciplinary team. Patients pay for health care on a sliding fee scale. Medications are provided in several ways. Pharmaceutical representatives and private doctor's offices donate sample medication. Pharmaceutical companies provide name brand medicine for chronic illness through an application process that must prove the patient to be medically indigent. Although this process is long and cumbersome, it allows many people to take medication that would otherwise be unaffordable. Also the clinic has a small stock of inexpensive generic medicines that it provides to patients.

In addition to a support staff of two licensed practical nurses and a medical assistant, the clinic employs a social worker who provides case management and counseling to patients with mental illness. Dietitians- and pharmacists-in-training at a local university help patients with diet and medication education. A provider is on call nights and weekends to advise on medical issues that arise.

Mr. Johnson and Mr. Whitman are two examples of people who found a "medical home" at the Craig Health Center (see inset

Teaching points from the HIV/AIDS portion of the Lay Health Promoter training course include:
• How HIV is and is not transmitted
• Risk factors for contracting HIV
• How transmission is prevented
• Basic understanding of how the virus works in the body
• Differentiating HIV from AIDS
• The importance of testing for HIV and location of test sites in the area
• Anonymous versus confidential testing
• How to interpret "negative" results
• HIV and pregnancy
• Treatment and Management of HIV/AIDS
• Advocating for persons with HIV/AIDS
• Community resources related to HIV/AIDS

boxes on this).

Lay Health Promotion

An approach which began in the third world is the use of specially trained members of the target population to provide one-on-one health education (Sung et al. 1997). Begun in 1994, Cross Over Ministry's Lay Health Promoter program teaches individuals in high-risk communities to improve the health knowledge of their neighbors and to show them how to seek medical care appropriately. This program is successful because it engages trusted members from inside the community who are able to bridge language and cultural gaps. The 40-hour training course for lay health promoters includes information on medical resources, instruction on subjects like healthy eating habits, domestic violence recognition, sexually transmitted diseases—including HIV and AIDS—and signs and symptoms of illness. Trainees are also taught physical exam skills such as how to measure blood pressure.

As a weekly class requirement, lay health promoters talk with others in their neighborhoods about health problems and share information on a subject in which they have recently been trained. According to Marilyn Metzler, the registered nurse who supervises the program, participants have reported over 41,000 health education contacts and numerous physician referrals, resulting in many diagnoses, which may not otherwise have been made.

"The decisions we make can affect us positively or negatively for the rest of our lives," states Ms. F., a lay health promoter who is passionate about giving people information so they can make good decisions. She orchestrated a health education program for a neighborhood in Richmond where most of the residents are Spanish speaking. The program, entitled "Abre Tus Ojos" (Open Your Eyes), provided facts about HIV/AIDS and other sexually transmitted diseases. "Our culture is not accustomed to talking about prevention of illness, and discussions about sex and illnesses caught through sexual activity tend to be taboo." She and other Spanish-speaking lay health promoters went door-to-door recruiting people to attend the seminar. Twenty people participated; a male physician facilitated the group of men, and a female physician assistant facilitated the group of women.

Case Management To Improve Children's Health—CHIP

Since 1997, the CHIP program (Children's Health Involving Parents) has taken a holistic approach into the homes of low-income families with young children. The model targets families with difficult social situations that interfere with their children's health. According to Sandy Graves, R.N., director of clinical services, "The parents want what's best for their kids but are in really difficult circumstances. Our task is to act as a resource and provide support." The nurse case manager evaluates the health needs of the child in the context

of his or her family and then provides support in areas such as guidance with parenting, helping obtain eligibility for health care services, and coordinating medical and mental health referrals. Other team members act as resources in areas like household management and budgeting, housing, and employment.

Conclusion

As this article points out, any truly successful, long-term solution to inner city health problems will require attention at many points. The single change that would make the greatest impact is the elimination of disparities in health care access between rich and poor. As health care providers, we must lobby for change and bear in mind the five key principles that can help improve the health of the inner city poor: providing quality medical care for free or on a fee sliding scale, offering services that are valued by the community they serve, acknowledging the constraints of the population, building on individual strengths, and partnering with other community resources.

Contact Information
Sandy Graves, R.N., FNP
Children's Health Involving Parents
101 Cowardin Ave., Suite 307
Richmond, VA 23224
804-233-2850
graves_sandra@yahoo.com

Marilyn Metzler, R.N.
Lay Health Promoters Program
of the Cross Over Ministry
108 Cowardin Ave.
Richmond, VA 23224
804-233-9167
lhp@crossoverministry.org

Judy Parker-Falzoi, R.N., FNP
Craig Health Center
8000 Brook Rd.
Richmond, VA 23227
804-264-2986
judyfalzoi@comcast.net

QUESTIONS FOR DISCUSSION

1. Consider the health issues and barriers to health care faced by the inner city poor that were identified in this article. In what ways have you encountered these issues in your own experience?

2. What are some creative ways health care providers might respond to noncompliance, crisis mode behaviors and the social situations of the urban poor?

3. What do you think is the most important impact of community-based health delivery models? Describe some ways you think these models make a difference in people's lives.

4. Describe any community-based health care clinic(s) available in the community where you live. Which of the five key factors identified in this article are utilized by your local clinic(s)? Which factors would you like to see implemented in your area?

5. Imagine that you have an opportunity to get involved in one of the programs Eddy describes. Which one interests you the most? Explain why.

SCENARIOS FOR LEARNING AND GROWTH

Read through the following scenarios and be prepared to answer these questions about them with the members of your group.

1. Which of the scenarios gave you the most insight regarding the health care problems of the poor? Why do you feel this way? Explain your answer to the group.

2. Which of the individuals described would you enjoy meeting personally? Why do you think this why?

Mr. Johnson was a very sick man three years ago. He had been without medicine for his diabetes for almost six months, since losing his job and health coverage. Although he had found a new job, it was without medical benefits; he was unable to afford insurance, doctor visits, or medicine. When he was first evaluated at Craig Health Center, he was dehydrated, had a very high glucose level, and a badly infected ulcer on his right great toe. The nurse practitioner was able to follow him closely, obtain the medicine that he needed, and get a specialist to evaluate his toe. In addition, he learned the importance of a sound diet from the dietitian. Although he eventually had to have the toe amputated, he is now doing well and comes in for diabetes checks only every three months or so. He doesn't really miss the days when he "just about lived at the clinic," but he does appreciate the calls he gets from the nurses between visits. "They call to make sure I'm okay. It's like a family.

Mr. Whitman wasn't sure life was worth living. A year ago, he was advised by the nurse practitioner to quit his job as a driver for a well-known package delivery company because peripheral neuropathy made him unable to reliably feel the gas pedal or brake. His feet burned relentlessly, but the pain medicine made him drowsy, so he couldn't take it while he was at work. By the age of 56, he had twice applied for disability benefits through the state but had been turned down, ostensibly because he was continuing to work. "If I stop working, I will have no money to live on," Mr. Whitman said with dismay. His depression was difficult to treat; but pain control and a small monthly check to pay for food and rent did wonders. The clinic found a lawyer to help him prove to the state that he is disabled, but it is a long, difficult process. He feels that the folks at the clinic are strong advocates for him, and that gives him hope.

Judah, an 18-year-old Sudanese refugee, was scared. He had been feeling nauseated and was very short of breath. He attempted to make an appointment with a private physician, but was turned away because he had no health insurance or money to pay. He called Mrs. J., a woman from the church that had sponsored him. Mrs. J. was a lay health promoter who knew the health care resources in Richmond well; she was able to get him into a free clinic the next day, where he was diagnosed with acute renal failure and dangerously high blood pressure. He was admitted to the hospital and treated with dialysis. Mrs. J. continued to advocate for him in the hospital, attempting to get him emergency medical insurance so that he would be able to continue dialysis after leaving the hospital.

Justin was the tiniest 4-year-old Dr. E had ever seen. His mother brought him in because of dry skin, and when the physician plotted out his height and weight on the growth chart, he was far below the 5th percentile for both. He also didn't have intelligible speech. When questioned about his food intake, it seemed that he ate enough food. His three-year-old sister came to the office visit also and was an outgoing, cheerful, verbal child with normal growth.

After illness was ruled out as a cause of the growth retardation, Dr. E. called in CHIP to evaluate the family. The nurse found that the family was homeless and living in a spare room at the home of another family. They were unable to use the kitchen or to bathe. While the mother worked full-time, the woman of the house would watch Justin and his sister along with six to eight other kids. He was unable to speak up for himself in order to get a meal, and the more malnourished he got, the less he tried to get food. When his mother was with him, he ate because she encouraged him, so she assumed he ate well while she was at work. The CHIP case manager helped the family obtain adequate shelter and day care. She was able to get Justin an evaluation with a Developmental Pediatrician who found him speech delayed and borderline mentally retarded. He responded well to speech therapy. Within a year the family had housing, the child began to grow, and he could tell Dr. E. about himself in short sentences.

Janae is breathing a little easier these days. She is a 2-year-old diagnosed with asthma at 18 months of age. After Janae's fourth emergency room visit for an asthma attack, CHIP was called by an ER social worker. The nurse from CHIP found that Janae lived with her 17-year-old mother and her grandparents. Environmental assessment revealed multiple modifiable asthma triggers in the home. She had no medical provider other than the emergency room, so the nurse and team taught her mother how to modify the asthma triggers and helped her obtain a physician. She has had no further ER visits or hospitalizations in the six months since CHIP became involved.

REFERENCES

Anderson, E. 1999. *Code of the Street.* New York: W.W. Norton & Company, Inc.

Andrulis, D. P. 1998. Access to care is the centerpiece in the elimination of socioeconomic disparities in health. *Annals of Internal Medicine* 129:412-416.

Blumenthal, D., E. Mort, and J. Edwards. 1995. The efficacy of primary care for vulnerable population groups. *HSR: Health Services Research* 30 (1): 253-273.

Blumenthal, D. S., J. Sung, R. Coates, J. Williams, and J. Liff. 1995. Recruitment and retention of subjects for a longitudinal cancer prevention study in an inner-city black community. *HSR: Health Services Research* 30 (1): 197-205.

Derose, K. P., and D. W. Baker. 2000. Limited English proficiency and Latinos' use of physician services. *Medical Care Research and Review* 57 (1): 76-91.

Freeman, H. P., and T. A. Alshafie. 2002. Colorectal carcinoma in poor blacks. *Cancer* 94 (9): 2327-32.

Graham, L. M. 2004. All I need is the air that I breathe: Outdoor air quality and asthma. *Pediatric Respiratory Review* 5, Supplement A: S59-64.

McMillan, J. A., C. D. DeAngelis, R. Feigin, and J. B. Warshaw, eds. 1999. *Oski's Pediatrics.* 3rd ed. Philadelphia: Lippincott, Williams & Wilkins.

Newman, L. A., K. Carolin, M. Simon, M. Kosir, W. Hryniuk, R. Demers, A. GrossbartSchwartz, D. Visscher, W. Peters, and D. Bouwman. 2001. Impact of breast carcinoma on African-American women: The Detroit experience. *Cancer* 91 (9): 1834-1843.

Nyamathi, A. M., E. L. Dixon, W. Robbins, C. Smith, D. Wiley, B. Leake, D. Longshore, and L. Gelberg. 2002. Risk factors for Hepatitis C Virus infection among homeless adults. *Journal of General Internal Medicine* 17 (2): 134-143.

Powell, L. M., S. Slater, and F. J. Chaloupka. 2004. The relationship between community physical activity settings and race, ethnicity and socioeconomic status. *Evidence-Based Preventive Medicine* 1 (2): 135-144.

Sung, J. F. C., E. Alema-Mensch, and D. S. Blumenthal. 2002. Inner-city African American who failed to receive cancer screening following a culturally-appropriate intervention: the role of health insurance. *Cancer Detection and Prevention* 26:28-32.

Sung, J. F. C., D. S. Blumenthal, R. J. Coates, J. E. Williams, E. Alema-Mensch, and J. M. Liff. (1997). Effect of a cancer screening intervention conducted by lay health workers among inner city women. *American Journal of Preventive Medicine* 13:51-57.

Wenzel, S. L., J. S. Tucker, M. N. Elliott, G. N. Marshall, and S. L. Williamson. 2004. Physical violence against impoverished women: A longitudinal analysis of risk and protective factors. *Women's Health Issues* 14 (5): 144-154.

The Public Safety Net: Is It Effective?

by Linda Strickland

Summary: The public safety net system in the U.S. is intended to protect those who are truly in need and without resources. Strickland highlights significant factors of abuse and misuse that threaten to overwhelm the system, and confronts value-laden issues of choice, social behavior and attitude, that must be considered in resolving issues of poverty and related health concerns.

The impact of poverty on health is complex and requires creative, non-traditional approaches to find viable solutions. Unquestionably, there are those who need assistance and to whom society is obligated to provide support. Literature overwhelmingly contains the stories and statistics of those who are living in poverty and subsequently experience negative health consequences. In the desire to be advocates for patients, and to demonstrate the values of compassion and caring, it is possible to miss important components of the poverty and health problem in the United States.

The purpose of this paper is to create an awareness of less obvious factors influencing health care statistics in the United States, and to examine the effectiveness of the public safety net system. In the desire to improve the health of patients served, negative and unintended consequences may result by promoting and creating policies that culminate in the allocation of additional resources without contribution by the recipient, instituting entitlements without accountability, perpetuating systems that encourage dependency in those persons capable of self-reliance, and encouraging non-beneficial consumption of health care.

> The challenge is to create policy that minimizes distortions in private insurance, eliminates those who would defraud the system, encourages choices that improve personal and community health, and assists those truly in need.

Factors That Escalate Use of the Public Safety Net System

The public safety net system in the United States is intended to protect those people who are truly in need and without resources, and few would disagree that a

Linda Strickland, MSN, CNNP, RN has worked primarily in public safety net systems for over 35 years. In addition to her practice as a neonatal nurse practitioner, she has held positions in administration, and directed the clinical programs of the Indiana University National Center of Excellence in Women's Health, creating a women's health service line in a public safety net organization. She has been an adjunct faculty member for Indiana Wesleyan University for the past five years in both the undergraduate and graduate programs.

strong safety net system serves a noble purpose. In order to assure such a system is truly effective, it is important to carefully evaluate factors that have the potential to put undue stress on this system and threaten its true purpose.

Insurance Factors

Insurance in the U.S. is primarily provided through three sources: private employment, military/veterans, and Medicare/Medicaid. In all cases, the individual/family is ignorant of the actual cost of care. Without insurance or charity, particularly in the case of catastrophic illness or accident, very few persons could afford the advanced care modern medicine provides. However, by being blinded to the true cost of preventive and routine care, patients have little incentive or ability to work collaboratively with their providers to keep costs under control.

> By being blinded to the true cost of preventive and routine care, patients have little incentive or ability to work collaboratively with their providers to keep costs under control.

Hadley and Holahan (2003), along with numerous others, note how the presence of insurance increases medical care use. An historical study, The RAND Health Insurance Experiment in the 1970s, demonstrated that health care is used in direct correlation with the cost to the individual, regardless of whether or not the care is beneficial (Brook et al. 1983). Use rates for hospital care grew at a significantly higher rate than the population between 1997 and 2001. PriceWaterhouseCoopers (2003) presented a report showing the increased use rates of hospital care to be 34.4% of the 55.4% growth in hospital spending. Meanwhile, population growth was only 21%. The report attributed the growth in use to three areas: backlash secondary to easing of managed care restrictions on access, an aging population, and technology or the ability to do more things for more people.

On one hand, the data supports the fact that insurance provides the means for people to receive needed care. The counter argument, however, is that with insurance, the demand for unnecessary care increases and providers are consulted for problems once cared for by the individual or family. Estimates are that at least 30% of care provided is unnecessary (Ferguson 2002). In communities with Amish settlements, one can observe a demonstration of access to care without insurance, low consumption of unnecessary services, healthy lifestyle choices, and economic viability. "While they do not reject modern medicine or hospital care, it is not always their first choice" (Banks and Benchott 2001).

Legal Factors

There are other forces that contribute to the number of uninsured and the upward spiral of health care costs. One is the need to practice defensive medicine. How often are laboratory tests, diagnostic tests, or prescriptions written to address the legal aspects of care? Increasingly, providers for patients in every socioeconomic stratum are threatened with lawsuits. Every health care provider is acutely aware of the tension between appropriate care and the extra diagnostics or treatments performed to cover the legal aspects of care.

In a country with one lawyer per 406 persons[1], lawsuits are a daily part of the health care equation. Physician liability claims have risen 9.7% annually since 2000 and malpractice costs have risen 11.8% per year since 1975 (Insurance Information Institute 2005). It is difficult to believe physicians, nurses, and other providers are more negligent or less skilled than their 1975 counterparts. Rather, the rise in lawsuits represents a cultural shift not limited to, but definitely impacting, health care.

Problems and disputes once settled by neighbors and within communities now find their way into the courtroom.

This density of lawyers creates the need to find new avenues for generating revenue. Lawyers are able to encourage lawsuits via advertising directly to patients, particularly during daytime TV when many people who do not work are watching, thus adding to the lawsuit (greed) mentality. Ads which encourage people to sue for denied disability promote victimization rather than self-reliance. Clinicians find themselves in a precarious position, pressured to keep patients satisfied while patients continue to demand care, drugs, tests, or new technology which they may deem a health care right. The clinician faces the option of saying no to patients' demands and risking a lawsuit or deferring to patients' demands and escalating care use (Mundinger et al. 2004). These tensions are present in safety net organizations serving the indigent as well as in not-for-profit health settings. A thorough examination of the defensive medicine and lawsuit mentality phenomena is beyond the scope of this paper. However, these issues should be a part of any comprehensive discussion of strategies for addressing the problem of the uninsured and health care costs, as they consume significant resources.

Opting Out of Available Options

Another development of interest includes those who opt not to pay for insurance even when it is available. This group includes those who change jobs and choose not to continue health care coverage through the period of unemployment despite the availability of COBRA (instituted by the Consolidated Omnibus Budget Reconciliation Act of 1985), those uninsured with incomes above the poverty level, those who are able-bodied but who choose not to work or to work part-time, and those

who choose to rely on emergency room and charity care, opting out of paying an insurance premium for care they expect to need (Mundinger et al. 2004). COBRA does not provide favorable tax treatment analogous to employer-provided insurance and the premiums are expensive as they include the portion of the premium paid by the employer (Gruber and Mandrian 2001). While low- and middle-income people may not be able to afford the COBRA coverage, those in the upper-middle and upper-income ranges can certainly afford it. Expense is often the stated reason for non-participation. However, the true reason may be closer to the economic term of utility, or the indifference curve; the total satisfaction received from a good or service (Mansfield and Yohe 2003). The desire for insurance appears to be less than the desire for other goods and services.

While 38-44 million uninsured is a frequently quoted statistic, the specific persons in that overall number are more fluid than static. It is not surprising that young, healthy adults with little health care risk would

> The desire for insurance appears to be less than the desire for other goods and services.

opt out of COBRA coverage between jobs. According to the U.S. Census Bureau report, the average length of time without insurance was 5.6 months. In addition, the approximately 15% of the population that is uninsured is not homogeneous. Of households in the $50,000 to $74,999 income bracket, 11.8% were uninsured in 2002, and 12.5% in 2003. (DeNavas-Walt, Proctor, and Mills 2004).

The data are even more striking in the $75,000 or over income bracket where 8.2% were uninsured in 2002 and 2003. If the two groups are combined, approximately 20% of households with incomes over $50,000 are uninsured (DeNavas-Walt, Proctor, and Mills 2004). It is difficult to make the case that a household with an income of $75,000 cannot afford insurance. For a family of four, $75,000 is slightly greater than 400% of federal poverty guidelines for 2003. Few studies have been done in this population to identify the reasons for lack of insurance. It has been documented that in communities with a Federally Qualified Health Center (FQHC) and other safety net care options, some people above the poverty guidelines will opt out of private insurance in favor of care at a FQHC (DeFrancesco 2004).

> "Crowd out" is the term applied when government programs become more desirable than private insurance. Public safety net systems are overwhelmed when people use the system inappropriately.

Safety Net "Crowd Out"

The phenomenon of safety net "crowd out" has been documented, particularly among unmarried, childless adults (DeFrancesco 2004). "Crowd out" is the term applied when government programs become more desirable than private insurance. Public safety net systems are overwhelmed when people use the system inappropriately. For some individuals, the utility of health insurance does not outweigh the utility of other desirable commodities. It becomes a circular argument: individuals do not purchase insurance because of the high cost of premiums, but 34-35% of the growth in hospital spending is a result of increased use rates, which spurs increases in insurance rates (PriceWaterhouseCoopers 2003). While there is limited data to explain the phenomena of "crowd out," those households who choose not to participate in available private insurance are counted as uninsured. In addition, the lack of participation by middle- and upper-middle income households removes those resources from the insurance pool and may influence employers' decisions regarding health care benefits (DeFrancesco 2004).

Some characteristics of welfare may create disincentives to work. Gruber and Madrian (2001) found that moving from welfare with Medicaid to a job without health insurance creates welfare lock. While policy reform has improved opportunities and encouraged employment, government programs with too-generous benefits have a negative impact on private insurance by "crowd out" (DeFrancesco 2004). There is data to support the fact that increased benefits in health insurance by employers raises the overall cost of health benefits, and leads to loss of entry level jobs.

In addition, as the imputed value of Medicaid rises, the value of maintaining Medicaid coverage creates a limited negative impact on the labor force participation of single mothers. However, other studies demonstrate that employer-provided health insurance decreases the median Medicaid spell by several months. (Gruber and Madrian 2001). It appears more study needs to be done in this area to assist in policy development. There is evidence, although the studies are limited, to support that health insurance influences married women's labor decisions. The availability of spousal health insurance reduces the labor force participation of married women by 6-20%. In fact, the availability of spousal insurance may reduce the probability of working full time, and increase the probability of working part-time, or working in a business without health insurance (Gruber and Madrian 2001).

Lessons from Norway and Sweden

There may be lessons to learn from Norway and Sweden regarding the interplay between an entitlement health insurance policy, productivity, and absenteeism. While Norway has one of the most generous sick pay benefits in the world, it ranks among the highest in days lost to absenteeism. It appears that the availability of compensation is a disincentive and encourages absenteeism (Nordberg and Roed 2003). The experience in Sweden and other European countries is similar. Since the implementation of generous sick benefits and national health policy, anywhere from 10-25% of workers are absent. In recent years, Sweden has moved from a traditional public monopoly for medical services to a diversity of producers, representing a return to privatization. Researchers have noted a return of normal labor market behavior, entrepreneurial values, and the incentives that accompany privatization and co-ownership (Hjertqvist 2002). The experience of Norway and Sweden demonstrate that entitlement programs may not provide motivation for self-reliance or produce the best result over the long term.

The Impact of Value Issues and Personal Choice

How discussion of the uninsured is framed changes the dimensions discussed. While trying to positively impact a problem once it has occurred is honorable and necessary, true problem resolution only occurs if the mitigating factors are addressed. The discussion and development of strategies to support the uninsured and unemployed are not value or morally neutral, despite multiple attempts to create a neutral environment. Personal choice often contributes to poverty and being uninsured.

Values Related to Family Structure and Education

One of the most significant predictors of poverty is being born out of wedlock (Rector 1999). In the mid 1960s, 8% of children were born out of wedlock; by the late 1990s the percentage quadrupled to 32% and is currently at 34% (Federal Interagency Forum on Child and Family Statistics 2004), despite widespread use and availability of birth control pills and condoms. The data further delineates that never-married mothers are about 10 years younger than divorced mothers and only 61% of never-married mothers have a high school diploma (U.S. Congress 1995). While the number of children born to teenagers has declined since the mid-1990s, the poverty rate remains high for those who are and is especially striking for African-American children. When divorce, separation, imprisonment, and death are considered, about 60% of poor families are headed by single mothers (Ellwood and Jencks 2002). Is it possible that a lack of moral compass has contributed to the rise of a cultural norm which is detrimental personally, to the children, and to society as a whole?

The role of education should not be underestimated in the poverty cycle. There ares data to support the view that education delays the time until childbirth; college graduates with first births at age 25 fell from 47% in the 1940s to 20% in the 1960s. Over the last decade, non-marital births rose fastest in the least educated women. Obviously, education increases economic opportunity and stability (Ellwood and Jencks 2002). Statistical data verifies the fact that education opens doors for a future with multiple possibilities. However, education does not always correlate with good health choices—consider cigarette smoking and alcohol consumption.

> One of the most significant predictors of poverty is being born out of wedlock.

Studies correlate the presence of both biological parents with children who perform better on school achievement tests, have fewer children as teenagers themselves, tend to complete high school, attend college more often, have greater earnings as young adults, and are less likely to live in poverty (Ellwood and Jencks 2002). It is less clear why those differences exist, but they may in fact be characteristics of people who are capable of maintaining long-term relationships.

The child development aspect of the demographics of poverty cannot be discussed in a vacuum of value neutrality. As Ellwood and Jencks (2002) point out, parents most often make choices to improve their own welfare or happiness. For instance, children's long-term welfare may be improved if 80% of parents stayed married or lived together until their children were grown, while parents' happiness might be maximized when only 40% stay together. Society has taken a hands-off stance, allowing each parent to do as he or she sees fit; a laissez-faire policy that has produced a 50% split rate and may not be serving children well. Perhaps more attention should be paid to creating policy to support intact families as marriage and childbirth are being disassociated.

> Work is a method of defining one's existence and to be denied the opportunity to work is to be treated as less than human.

In 1965, never being married was rare, but by 2002, nearly 25% of mothers without high school diplomas had never been married (Ellwood and Jencks 2002). Non-marital birth rates have risen in most affluent nations; in Sweden non-marital births are twice as common as in the U.S.. However, most unmarried parents in Sweden raise their children together, thus the majority of children live with both biological parents (Ellwood and Jencks 2002). The role of culture, personal choice, and values should not be eliminated or underestimated in the discussions of poverty and health.

The politically correct milieu seeks to create a value-neutral environment for policy discussion and ignore the moral implications of the choices people make. However, the reality is that the decision to have a child out of wedlock, prior to earning a high school diploma, has moral relevance by contributing significantly to a life of poverty for the mother and the child, poorer developmental outcomes for the children, and moral dilemmas. To add the values dimension to the discussion is not to ignore the vision and hopes of those who have made an error or to abandon those in need. It is, however, to challenge a system which behaves as though there is no moral component to the discussion. If the family is the "foundation for stability, understanding and social peace," as stated by Moynihan (1986) then the moral implications of choice and personal responsibility are required to be part of the discussion. It is crucial to consider whether current policy or more generous health benefits in the absence of accountability, personal contribution, and moral or cultural change will accomplish the intended goals.

Values in the Marketplace

While the argument is made that mandatory work by welfare recipients has only slightly improved their economic status, particularly in the light of the recent economic downturn (Sherman, Fremstad, and Parrott 2004), little attention is given to the role of work as fulfilling and meaningful apart from the monetary reward. Wong (2003) discusses the intrinsic value of work as creative, redemptive, and impacting the world in the future. Work is a method of defining one's existence and to be denied the opportunity to work is to be treated as less than human. Work is necessary to sustain life; people obtain food, clothing, and shelter as a result of labor. All work is meaningful unless it is illegal, immoral, or unethical. Current culture de-emphasizes the importance of work for work's sake and elevates the value of leisure time (Wong 2003). A valid argument can be made that the majority of the uninsured are working;

therefore policy formation and society at large should reward and support those who are working. However, of the uninsured between the ages of 18-64, there remains the roughly 26% who are not working and another 24% who work part-time (DeNavas-Walt, Proctor, and Mills 2004). Different policies and creative ideas are necessary to address the needs of this population. In other words, one size does not fit all (DeFrancesco 2004).

The data regarding non-working adults provides a challenge. There are insufficient data available regarding the reasons for non-working or part-time status. However, it seems improbable that 26% of the uninsured between the ages of 18-64 were too disabled to work.

Single mother employment for 2003 was 69.8%; another 10.2% was available to the labor force but unemployed, leaving around 20% of single mothers neither in the labor force nor seeking employment. Job loss was 3.3% among single mothers and 3.5% among never married mothers during the economic downturn of 2001-2003 (Sherman, Fremstad, and Parrott 2004). Yes, the availability of jobs impacts employment; however, one cannot exclude choosing not to work as one explanation for the 20% of single mothers who are not working. The public safety net system takes up the slack when able-bodied people choose not to work. More research needs to be done regarding the uninsured unemployed and the role of personal responsibility and choice.

It is clear minorities are disproportionately represented in poverty statistics. However, there is another side to this story. The untold story is one of economic opportunity created by African-American entrepreneurs. They have done more to improve the economic status for the African-American community than politicians or traditional pastors. Today, most African-

Americans are members of the middle class, 40% live in suburbs and 17% of adult African-Americans hold college degrees, compared to 20% of all adult Americans. African-Americans are 50% more likely than Whites to be entrepreneurs. While politics and policy have failed to create economic opportunity, the entrepreneurs are creating businesses that promote prosperity and spur economic development (Bradley 2003). Perhaps the politicians, health care providers, and other community leaders need to take lessons from African-American businessmen. Economic opportunity coupled with personal responsibility may decrease poverty, increase insurance availability, and improve health more than any government entitlement program.

Ferguson (2002) makes a strong argument that more market forces, not fewer, should assist in regulating health care supply and demand, including for the poor. He argues that increased market forces will make more economical health care available for the poor and contends that consumers and providers are capable of making the right choices regarding health care in the areas of prevention and ambulatory care, excluding catastrophic illness. The market will adjust prices based on supply and demand. While the market may not control supply and costs for catastrophic illness, it remains to be seen if market forces will control ambulatory services. A recent trend in ambulatory services being offered for cash in supermarkets and retail stores appears to be successful. Some sites now contract for ambulatory care with insurance companies. A nurse practitioner (NP) or physician assistant (PA) provides care for walk-in patients for a cash fee between $39 and $45, or for a co-pay. The care is much quicker, more convenient for patients, and provided

> *The public safety net system takes up the slack when able-bodied people choose not to work.*

at lower cost with lower overhead (Cain 2004). The NP or PA has access to a consulting physician and refers complicated care to an office or clinic. This type of site provides easy access for poor patients who are unable to leave work for appointments. In addition, patients can shop while they wait for care by carrying a pager.

While mandatory coverage by businesses may appear to be a viable solution, mandating coverage backfires. Mandated health coverage for specific illnesses results in a loss of insurance. In 1965, health insurance had an average of 8 mandatory services. In the last 40 years, the number of mandated services has escalated to over 1,400. Most of the demands for added services did not come from enrollees but from providers lobbying legislators to cover their services. Approximately 1 in 4 uninsured Americans has been priced out of the market by increased insurance mandates (Goodman 2003). Since the majority of Americans work for small business, mandates impact the most vulnerable part of the market. A return to basic insurance coverage would reduce the number of uninsured by 25%!

> *Addressing problems after the fact is similar to trying to mend the damage after a stroke.*

Conclusions

The impact of poverty on health is clearly negative and deserves attention and creativity to find strategies that create desired outcomes. The why and how of poverty and being uninsured is complex, as are most human conditions. Buried in the familiar statistics are subsets of people who do not fit the standard profile of those in need. Social behavior, cultural norms, values, and age-old human behavior also factor in this dilemma.

The challenge is to create policy that minimizes distortions in private insurance, eliminates those who would defraud the system, encourages choices that improve personal and community health, and assists those truly in need. Perhaps the time has come to create separate payment schemes for preventive and ambulatory care versus hospital and specialized, high-technology care. Given that it is possible to eliminate the 30% of care which is unnecessary, society must develop efficient ways to distribute the resources to those who are in need.

New methods and strategies for encouraging choices promoting health, avoiding non-marital pregnancy, improving family stability, encouraging education, and avoiding poverty are needed. Addressing problems after the fact is similar to trying to mend the damage after a stroke. The best strategy to improve the outcome of patients is prevention. The economic health of the nation should not be underestimated as an important partner in achieving health goals. There is opportunity and hope as new strategies emerge to improve individual health status, family and community health, and the health of the nation.

RESOURCES:

The Robert Wood Johnson Foundation:
http://www.rwjf.org/index.jsp

The Henry J. Kaiser Family Foundation:
http://www.kff.org/

National Center for Policy Analysis:
http://www.ncpa.org/

Center on Budget and Policy Priorities:
http://www.cbpp.org/

Acton Institute for the Study of Religion and Liberty:
http://www.acton.org/

The Heritage Foundation:
http://www.heritage.org/

U.S. Census Bureau:
http://www.census.gov/

Federal Interagency Forum on Child and Family Statistics:
http://www.childstats.gov/ac2004/intro.asp

QUESTIONS FOR DISCUSSION

1. What individuals/groups are not protected by the Public Safety Net in the United States? Why does it fail to meet their needs?

2. What lessons about the Public Safety Net could we learn from Norway and Sweden?

3. Some of the research reviewed in this article describes a relationship between family structure and the incidence of poverty among children. Why do you feel there is a correlation between the two? What can families do to keep their children from becoming poor?

4. Professor Strickland refers to a work by B.S. Ferguson (2002) who believes that "more market forces, not fewer, should assist in regulating health care supply and demand." Do you agree with this statement? Why or why not?

5. "Perhaps the time has come to create separate payment schemes for preventive and ambulatory care versus hospitalized and specialized high technology care." Do you agree with this statement? Why or why not?

NOTES

1. This statistic is revrived from the U.S. Department of Labor's Bureau of Labor Statistics. It is base on 695,000 lawyers employed in the U.S. in 2002 and the U.S. population from the 2000 census (U.S. Department of Labor 2005).

SCENARIOS FOR LEARNING AND GROWTH

Read through the following scenarios and discuss the questions that follow them with the members of your group.

CASE STUDY ONE—WHO IS UNINSURED?

V. and S. are both 25 years old and have been married two and a half years. S. worked part-time and operated a small business. Once her small business began to thrive she quit her part-time job.

Until recently, V. worked part-time, 20 hours/week, at a health care organization and did freelance work on the side. V. had been eligible to carry S. and himself on a health insurance policy purchased through the health care organization. Six months ago, V. was hired full-time by an organization that liked his freelance work. There was a six-month waiting period for insurance eligibility at the new organization. V. and S. have decided not to purchase insurance through COBRA during this time; they are both healthy and feel the most likely adverse event they might face is a car accident. They are covered for car accidents on their car insurance.

With the new job, the couple decided to buy a new $24,000 car. Several months ago they decided to sell the two-bedroom home they purchased when they were married and build a new one with more space, for approximately $135,000. With the proceeds of the sale of their home, they purchased new furniture and appliances. They also traded in S.'s SUV for a used $20,000 SUV and put $5,000 down.

V. is now eligible for health insurance. However, they decided it was too expensive to pay the premiums for both of them to be covered. Their annual household income is approximately $70,000.

V. and S. are counted in the number of uninsured Americans. There is no law mandating health insurance coverage, and there is nothing about their current health status that is vulnerable; they are healthy, they are making money, they are making personal choices.

Questions:
1. How would you evaluate V. and S.'s choice regarding health insurance?

2. If you had a chance to advise V. and S., what would you tell them?

3. If either V. or S. becomes ill and they need financial assistance to pay their bills, what kind of help should they be allowed to receive from the public safety net system?

CASE STUDY TWO—SELF-EMPLOYED, SELF-INSURED

L. is a 50-year-old single man who decided to change to part-time work at his regular place of employment so he could start doing some part-time freelance work. As a part-time employee, he was no longer eligible for health insurance through his workplace. He attempted to obtain an individual health insurance policy through numerous private companies, but because of some pre-existing health problems, he was rejected by each of them. In spite of the pre-existing health problems, L. was in good health overall. He learned that he was eligible for health insurance through a state-run insurance pool for people like himself, who were unable to find insurance through private insurers. This insurance was managed but not funded by the state, so the cost was more than double the price he would have paid for other individual policies. Without an employer to pay a portion of the insurance, he knew he would have to pay the full price of the insurance himself, making the cost of health insurance extremely high. In addition, he expected his total income to decrease for a period of time as he developed his freelance work. After weighing his options, L. decided that it was important to obtain the insurance through the state-run pool, even though it was costly. He adjusted his personal budget, gave up many nonessentials, and simplified his lifestyle in many ways, in order to pay the high monthly fee.

1. How would you evaluate L.'s choice regarding health insurance? What other alternatives for health care coverage would you suggest for him?

2. If you were in the same position, would you have made the same choice as L., or not? Explain your reasons.

3. How would you evaluate L.'s decision compared to V. and S.'s decision in case study one?

4. L. must pay for his health insurance through his own after-tax income, while a portion of the taxes he pays is used to fund uninsured people. Should L. be given a tax break for paying his own health insurance?

CASE STUDY THREE—WELFARE TO WORK

The following is a true case; however, the name has been changed to protect identity. J. is 23 years old with two children, ages three and five, with different fathers. J. was raised by her grandmother, because her mother was addicted to drugs; her mother also lives with the grandmother.

J. has never held a steady job. J.'s case worker assisted her in obtaining her GED (general equivalency diploma) and helped her enroll in a welfare to work program. The program places enrollees in a "volunteer" work setting with the opportunity to become employed. J. is quite bright and mastered the skills necessary for the job rather quickly. But there was a significant misstep — J. did not show up or call one day. J. was counseled regarding the importance of calling in when ill or late. She was subsequently hired full-time. With her first paycheck, J. had her hair braided and got a manicure. She had no bank account.

Initially, J. met expectations well with coaching. However, episodes of tardiness became more frequent. One morning, J. parked in a no-parking zone and her car was impounded. Furthermore, J. was driving without a license, which had been revoked for unpaid driving fines. Several people in the department volunteered to pick her up and bring her to work. For several months, the staff assisted her in getting to work. It was necessary to call J. 30 minutes prior to picking her up to be sure she and the children were ready.

J. lived with a current boyfriend in Section 8 housing, although it was prohibited—he had several arrests including jail time for drug dealing. Suspicion ran high among the staff at work that J. was experiencing domestic violence; despite encouragement from the staff and appeals regarding the well being of her girls, nothing changed. One day, a neighbor reported her violations and the Section 8 housing was revoked. She had to move. Her grandmother would not allow J. to live with her again. For valid reasons, her other relatives would not allow her to live with them. The staff assisted J. in finding a homeless shelter. At the shelter, there were structure and specific expectations for J. and the children. J. also received counseling in handling finances, debt management, legal entanglements, parenting skills, and household management.

In the meantime, there were intermittent episodes of not calling in, tardiness, and reports of not being friendly to clients. Each time, J. was counseled, a plan of action was initiated, and problem solving was explored. J.'s first response was often to quit, but when other alternatives were presented, J. would choose one of the alternatives. To assist with her situation, J.'s hours were changed. This change provided better opportunity to get the children to day care and arrive at work on time. Expectations for employee behavior were continually reinforced, firmly but with encouragement. Staff also assisted her in having her child transferred to a more convenient school, establishing a bank account, and on occasion cared for her children so she had a day to herself.

When J. smiles, she can light up the whole room. She definitely has the capacity to return to school, learn a profession or additional skills. At one point, she asked a staff member how to receive the Lord into her heart; she received the Lord but has not integrated into a church community. J. has no friends with whom she spends time. When not at work, she is at her grandmother's. J. has been gaining confidence and considering returning to school. The longer J. works, the more confidence she gains in her ability to care for herself and her family. The organization has an employee mentor program and J. was paired with a mentor. In addition, the organization has an employee assistance program and J. was given information to access the program. It is unknown if she utilized the service as it is confidential.

With the help of those running the shelter, the Section 8 housing eligibility was restored. J. moved into an apartment and her interest in returning to school was robust. However, she cbecame pregnant again; the father was the drug dealer. At first, she refused to accept personal responsibility, but little by little she faced the facts. As she accepted responsibility and formulated a plan, she gained some sense of control. School obviously was delayed, but she continued to work. The staff initially felt betrayed, but subsequently supported her with a shower, encouraged her to return to work, and helped her to problem solve.

J. returned to work after 8 weeks of maternity leave and continues to work full time; she states she feels accountable to everyone who has helped her. She still talks about the day when she will be able to return to school. Work is often a struggle, but she holds onto the hope to make a different life for herself and her children. She recently allowed the last child's father to move into her apartment.

QUESTIONS
1. Should employers be expected to "go the extra mile" to help welfare to work employees make the transition?

2. What is the role of servant leadership in J.'s integration into the work place?

3. What are reasonable accommodations or support at work? When does the support have a negative impact on other staff members?

At times, the staff wanted to see J. fired; at times it appeared she wanted to be fired, and occasionally it seemed doubtful she would survive in the workforce.
4. How would you counsel J. regarding her performance? What documentation is needed?

5. How important do you believe it was for J. to take personal responsibility for her choices?

6. What is the role of accountability in successful transition to work?

Continued on next page

J. related that her family thinks she is crazy for working. They do not offer any assistance.

7. *How do personal relationships contribute to success or failure of the transition?*

8. *What rewards, other than money, are important to employee retention for people like J.?*

9. *Are organizational mentoring programs important for entry level workers?*

J. stated, "Working is much harder than I thought it would be." Prior to working, she had unlimited time to do whatever she wanted. She shares that it is hard to smile at everyone when she is discouraged. She admits she sometimes resents those who seem to have so much more than she does and yet they complain.

10. *Where should people learn the skills which middle-class children learn at home?*

11. *How would you reply to J. when she is discouraged?*

12. *Does government welfare, by its very nature, build accountability and self-reliance or foster entitlement?*

13. *Would community or church-based programs increase personal accountability and increase motivation to remain in the workforce?*

CASE STUDY FOUR—ENTITLEMENT VS. RESPONSIBILITY?

K., 21, presents to the hospital in premature labor. She is carrying twins and is currently 24 weeks gestation. She is diagnosed with placenta previa and advised to remain in the hospital until she delivers. K., however, becomes bored in the hospital and signs herself out AMA. Within a week, K. is readmitted and delivers 25-week-old twins. (It is important to note that K. may have remained in the hospital and still delivered at 25 weeks gestation.) Both of the twins are intubated and placed on respirators. Over the course of the next 48 hours, Twin B becomes significantly worse and requires high frequency ventilation. Within the next couple of days, Twin B develops an interventricular hemorrhage (IVH), grade III-IV. Both twins develop sepsis in the course of their hospitalization requiring antibiotics. Twin B with the IVH develops hydrocephalus and requires a ventricular-peritoneal shunt. Both twins are at high risk for developmental delay, but especially Twin B. The first twin is hospitalized for 12 weeks and the second twin is hospitalized for 18 weeks, at a cost of over $300,000, not including the continued medical/surgical care which will be required. In addition, Twin A has about a 50% chance of developmental delay and Twin B has a greater than 50% chance of developmental delay requiring special education or additional resources.

K. is not married and does not work. Her boyfriend and father of the twins, 21-year-old M., is also not employed. K. was on Medicaid for her pregnancy; the other children are on a state-funded health insurance plan. K. had two previous children removed from her custody. She and her boyfriend rarely visit, perhaps because of transportation problems. They are both healthy and have no debilitating diseases. However, K. and M. request no phone calls before 11 a.m. because K. is not up until then.

The twins are K. and M.'s first children together. However, there are 7 children between them. K. does not have a high school diploma, although M. does. They live with K.'s mother.

QUESTIONS

1. *Who should pay for the twins' care?*

2. *What might be the impact of requiring volunteer or community service as some form of contribution toward the care received if K. and M. are not able to find work?*

3. *Should job training be mandated for K. and M.?*

4. *The current system does not allow working people to opt out of paying for K.'s and M.'s choices. What are the rights of those who work, sometimes more than one job, to care for their families? Should taxes continue to be increased so K. and M. can continue their present lifestyle?*

5. *Is justice served for K. and M. to continue to enlarge their family while other people pay the bill?*

6. *How can a system be designed to hold people accountable for their choices?*

REFERENCES

Banks, M. J., and R. J. Benchot. 2001. Unique aspects of nursing care for Amish children. [Electronic version]. MCH: *The American Journal of Maternal/Child Nursing* 26 (4): 192-196.

Bradley, A. B. 2003. The Rise of the Black entrepreneur: a new force for economic and moral leadership. Acton Institute for the Study of Religion and Liberty, May 7. http://www.acton.org/ppolicy/comment/article.php?id=137 (retrieved February 20, 2005).

Brook, R. H., J. E. Ware, W. H. Rogers, E. B. Keeler, A. R. Davies, C. A. Donald, G. A. Goldberg, K. N. Lohr, P. C. Masthay, and J. P. Newhouse. 1983. Does free care improve adult's health? Results from a randomized controlled trial. *New England Journal of Medicine* 309 (23): 1426-34.

Cain, Brad. 2004. Trends: Will that be cash or charge? *HealthLeaders*, July 2004. http://www.healthleaders.com/magazine/2004/jul/feature1.php?contentid= 56141&categoryid=153 (retrieved February 1, 2004).

DeFrancesco, L. 2004. Safety net "crowding out" private health insurance for childless adults. *Academy Health Findings Brief* 7 (3).

DeNavas-Walt, C., B. D. Proctor, and R. J. Mills. 2004. Income, poverty, and health insurance coverage in the United States: 2003. Current population reports, U.S. Department of Commerce, Economics and Statistics Administration, U.S. Census Bureau, 60-226.

Ellwood, D. T., and C. Jencks. 2002. The spread of single-parent families in the United States since 1960. John F. Kennedy School of Government, Harvard University. http://www.ksg.harvard.edu/inequality/Seminar/Papers/ElwdJnck.pdf (retrieved February 10, 2005).

Federal Interagency Forum on Child and Family Statistics. 2004. America's Children: Key National Indicators of Well-Being. http://www.Childstats.gov/ac2004/intro.asp (retrieved February 20, 2005).

Ferguson, B. S. 2002. *Issues in the demand for medical care: can consumers and doctors be trusted to make the right choices?* [Electronic version]. Halifax, Nova Scotia: Atlantic Institute for Market Studies.

Goodman, J. C. 2003. Health insurance mandates increase costs, uninsured. National Center for Policy Analysis. February 11. http://www.ncpa.org/abo/quarterly/ 20034th/clips/jg021103.html (retrieved February 4, 2005).

Gruber, J., and B. C. Madrian. 2001. Health insurance, labor supply, and job mobility: a critical review of the literature. Economic Research Initiative on the Uninsured Working Paper Series 4, University of Michigan, at Ann Arbor.

Hadley, J., and J. Holahan. 2003. How much medical care do the uninsured use, and who pays for it? *Health Affairs*. http://www.healthaffairs.org/ (retrieved February 1, 2004—search by authors).

Hjertqvist, J. 2002. When the employees take over…Employee ownership creeps into Sweden's health system. Swedish healthcare in transition. *Policy Frontiers* 4. Frontier Centre for Public Policy.

Insurance Information Institute, Inc. 2005. Medical malpractice. http://www.iii.org/media/hottopics/insurance/medicalmal/ (retrieved February 2, 2005).

Mansfield, E., and G. Yohe. 2003. *Microeconomics: Theory and applications.* 11th ed. New York: W. W. Norton & Company.

Moynihan, D. P. 1986. *Family and Nation.* New York: Harcourt, Brace, Jovanovich.

Mundinger, M. O., E. Thomas, J. Smolowitz, and J. Honig. 2004. Essential health care: Affordable for all? *Nursing Economics Journal* 22 (5):239-245.

Nordberg, M., and K. Rocd. 2003. Absenteeism, health insurance, and business cycles. University of Oslo Health Economics Research Programme Working Paper 17. http://www.hcro.uio.no/publicat/2003/HERO2003_17.pdf (retrieved February 15, 2003).

PriceWaterhouseCoopers. 2003. Cost of caring: Key drivers of growth in spending on hospital care. Presented to the American Hospital Association and the Federation of American Hospitals, Washington, DC. www.hospitalconnect.com/aha/press room-info/content/CostsReportSummary.ppt (retrieved February 15, 2005).

Rector, R. 1999. Illegitimacy is the major cause of child poverty. *Intellectual Ammunition* January/February. The Heartland Institute. http://www.heartland.org/Article.cfm/artId=403 (retrieved February 25, 2005).

Sherman, A., S. Fremstad, and S. Parrott. 2004. Employment rates for single mothers fell substantially during recent period of labor market weakness. Center on Budget and Policy Priorities. http://www.cbpp.org/6-22-04ui.htm (retrieved on January 22, 2005).

U.S. Congress. Senate Committee on Finance. 1995. Testimony on unmarried mothers and welfare reform. Given by Douglas J. Besharov on March 14, 1995. http://www.welfareacademy.org/ppubs/welfare/testimony 0395.shtml (retrieved February 18, 2005).

U.S. Department of Labor, Bureau of Labor Statistics. 2005. Occupational Outlook Handbook: Lawyers; employment http://www.bls.gov/oco/ocos053.htm (retrieved May 17, 2005).

Wong, S. L. 2003. The intrinsic value of work in the light of the doctrines of creation, redemption and eschatology. *Faith Business Quarterly* (7) 1. http://www.fibq.org /Faith%20in%20Business%20Quarterly%20-%20Sample%20Papers_files /The%20intrinsic%20value%20of%20work%20(Fibq7_1).pdf (Retrieved February 2, 2005).

Homelessness within Los Angeles County:
Health Care Initiatives in Shelter-based Clinics

by Connie Brehm

Summary: In this article, the author describes the ministry of Azusa Pacific University to the homeless in Los Angeles County. Emphasis is placed on the pathologies they encountered and the lessons they learned which can be applied to other communities with individuals who need health care support.

In the early 1990s homelessness received significant media attention in the Los Angeles area. Nearly every day the newspaper carried stories about the increasing numbers of homeless in the downtown area. Homelessness in the United States had not been seen on this scale for a number of decades. The post-World-War II prosperity of this country, as well as the many collective efforts to reduce poverty in the 1950s, 60s, and 70s resulted in an all time low number of homeless people. In the 90s, many individuals became homeless again.

As the decade began, I read an article in the *Los Angeles Times* about an entrepreneurial nurse practitioner on the faculty at UCLA School of Nursing. She had opened a storefront clinic in one area of downtown Los Angeles and was bringing nurse practitioner students with her to provide health care for the homeless. Her work

> In the early 1990s homelessness received significant media attention in the Los Angeles area.

caught my attention and planted a seed in my consciousness that would develop into a similar outreach effort for me and my students. This effort continues to this day.

In this article I will describe the homeless in Los Angeles County, the nature of our ministry to them and the pathologies we encountered in our work. My hope is that the lessons we have learned will be useful to others who seek to support those with needs through clinical interventions in their own communities.

Understanding the Homeless

Who are the homeless and what are their needs? This is the question we have asked ourselves as we ministered to them. Very few of them have cars or even enough bus tokens to rely on public transportation. They travel on foot from one location to the next as they search for food, water, a bathroom, and shelter for the night. These things, which most of us give little thought

Connie Brehm, RN, Ph.D., FNP, is Associate Professor of Nursing at Azusa Pacific University, located in Southern California. She is Director of the Homeless Outreach Clinic of the School of Nursing, and has been involved in bringing health care to the homeless for the past 10 years. She is the recipient of several grants that have supported homeless health care outreach.

to on a day-to-day basis, are major challenges for them. The meager income they earn comes from collecting cans and bottles and an occasional day of manual labor.

Not Welcome Here

In the late 1990s, the greatest need of the homeless was for shelter during the winter months. In the moderate climate of Southern California, many homeless build encampments along riverbeds or under bridges, which they prefer to overcrowded shelters, where they may feel dehumanized. From December to the middle of March, this is inadequate as temperatures drop into the 30s and 40s at night, accompanied by torrents of rain with frequent flooding.

With the increased number of homeless, local communities began exercising a policy called NIMBY (Not In My Back Yard) meaning that local law enforcement authorities force the homeless to move out of their town, and then they knock down their encampments. This has increased the need for year-round emergency shelters in Los Angeles County. In our area the Coalition for the Homeless only operates a winter shelter.[1] Since there is no permanent building available for the shelter, local churches allow the homeless to come inside their buildings for a meal and to sleep overnight (from 6:00 p.m. to 6:00 a.m.).

Homeless Families and Their Needs

Homeless families find it even more difficult to meet their needs. In the past they were allowed to spend the night in church shelters as well, but the County authorities who regulate the winter shelters have determined that they are not an appropriate environment for children. Sending homeless families to a motel works all right, as long as there are enough vouchers to go around. When the vouchers run out, as they tend to do toward the end of each month,

there is nothing to offer the families other than a meal. After they eat, they are turned out into the streets. Some families resort to sleeping in their cars, while those without transportation look for a place outside to sleep.[2] This is not an effective solution; many will stay awake all night because of fright and cold. As one young girl recalls, "We went behind a row of bushes and lay down next to a fence. We all huddled together to keep warm. We did not have any blanket. All we had was a sheet, so we put that over us. We were pretty cold, and it was kind of hard to sleep and we felt afraid."[3] Thirty-four-year-old pregnant Maria, with a 2 year old, described sleeping outside, as follows, "I found a spot in an alley. All I had was my jacket to keep warm. I had no blanket. So, we lay down next to a building and I pulled some garbage cans in front of us to hide us and provide a little more shelter. I held my son close to me all night, but could not sleep a wink." When I heard her account, I had to ponder what kind of a society we have become when pregnant women and young children are allowed to sleep in alleys.[4]

> What kind of a society have we become when pregnant women and young children are allowed to sleep in alleys?

Homeless people sleeping outside are subject to robbery, beatings (due to territoriality among the homeless), and victimization by gangs. Many chronically homeless persons who have managed to find a safe place to sleep outside at night will not divulge their secret spot to anyone, for fear it will be taken away from them. Homeless individuals found sleeping in the daytime are often doing so because they could not rest the night before.

Ministry to the Homeless, the Approach of Azusa Pacific University

Our first initiative in Hollywood came at the invitation of Dan Elliot, a fellow faculty

99

member in APU's School of Education. As an ordained minister, he conducted ministry part-time at a Nazarene Church in Hollywood. It was to this site that we first went out to see the homeless. Accompanied by three of my graduate students, I drove to Hollywood (a long journey in the L.A. afternoon rush hour traffic) to see how we could help with the health needs of the homeless. We hoped to pursue nursing practice and possibly develop the ministry into an additional clinical teaching site for nursing students, giving them experience with the desperately poor.

> Together we began to put together a plan to begin to address the health needs of the clients of the local Winter Shelter Program.

Through the fall and spring semesters of 1995-96, we traveled to the venue one night a week and provided health services. The room we used had one exam table, one cabinet full of donated medications (over-the-counter) and a few medical supplies. We brought our own assessment equipment and blood pressure cuffs. We had to arrive by 5:00 p.m. in order to park our cars in the lot, as it was locked down at dark. Cars parked on the street were vulnerable to theft and vandalism. Upon entering the facility, we walked through a waiting line of homeless people, went up the stairs to the second story, and set up our clinic in a room about the size of a double closet.

More than 100 people attended the services each night. I would look from person to person seated in the pews. Many had a real homeless look about them: weather-beaten faces, hair that looked singed from dryness, grimy skin and hair from days in the elements, a patina of dirt and oil coating their clothes. Some were dressed in flamboyant style, typical of Hollywood; that is, they wore bright exotic clothing with lots of make-up and jewelry, with brightly tinted hair to match. The mix in the group was about 2/3 men to about 1/3 women. We also observed some teens without parents, and even children there with their mothers and/or fathers. Their faces said they had experienced brokenness, anxiety, and challenging lives. I knew that only Jesus could help and I prayed that he would.

Moving the Ministry to the San Gabriel Valley

In the fall of 1997, during an incidental conversation with a public health nurse (PHN) at a nearby county health center, I was invited to join the newly formed health committee of the East San Gabriel Valley Coalition for the Homeless. The Coalition is a local nonprofit organization that operates the Winter Shelter Program, a program that provides emergency shelter on a night-to-night basis for the homeless of our area. The health committee was formed out of concern about contagious disease and other untreated health problems observed among the homeless who were using the shelter. The PHN shared, "We were seeing people at the shelter infected with lice at the start of the winter season, and four months later, the same people were still suffering with lice infestation." I began to attend the Coalition's Health Committee meetings along with several other community health professionals, from mental health and public health fields, and together we began to put together a plan to begin to address the health needs of the clients of the local Winter Shelter Program.

As our newly formed health committee got underway, we determined that each of us could address a specific health need. The county public health nurses said they would provide flu immunizations and TB screening. The representative from the Los Angeles County Department of Mental Health said she would send mental health caseworkers to the shelter to connect mentally ill clients with resources for care and medications. A representative from a local hospital said the hospital could provide supplies and pharmaceuticals for an outreach clinic in the shelter, but they could not spare any personnel to treat the clients.

Our Contribution to the Effort

What we, from APU School of Nursing, could offer was the nurse-power. My graduate students and I would treat clients. (Undergraduate nursing students now participate as well.) Our original plan was to set up our clinic at the shelter, perform health assessments, and treat the acute health problems of the shelter clients. Certified Nurse Practitioners (NPs) in the State of California are legally able to diagnose and treat medical problems of essentially healthy people, as long as there is a licensed physician available for consultation and collaboration by the NP.

Fortunately, the director of a local hospital emergency department, agreed to work with us. Though he was not present physically at our clinics, he agreed to be available by telephone. He also reviewed and approved the clinic protocols and performed the quality assurance review of clinic activities through case review and chart audits. This collaborative arrangement also permitted us to furnish pharmaceuticals for our clients, provided by the hospital free of charge. Our plan for clients with complicated, chronic health problems or emergent health problems was (and still is) to make referrals to local community clinics for care.

That first year, I had a class of 15 clinical FNP students. I allowed the students to sign up on a voluntary basis to go out with me to manage the clinic and see the clients. The first year we went out to the church shelter two nights a week for the season. Since the students signed up voluntarily, there were some nights that I did not have much help. However, I must gratefully acknowledge that there were two graduate students in my class who were very faithful about serving as many nights as they possibly could.

Since that first season, 1997-98, we have continued to operate our clinic in the church shelter each winter season (eight winters in all so far). As of the most recent season, 2005, we have now topped 1000 client visits to our shelter clinic. The APU faculty now stipulate that each FNP student is required to participate in our homeless shelter outreach clinic at least two nights during the winter season. This stipulation, in part, assures that we meet one of our Masters program goals; to teach students about how to serve the underserved.

Over the years, we have expanded our services offered for the clients. We now carry a much larger pharmacy with us. We know the health care resources in the community much better so we are able to make more effective referrals,

> *Each FNP student is required to participate in our homeless shelter outreach clinic at least two nights during the winter season.*

and we bring as many as 12-15 students with us (from all levels of our nursing program). We have now hired two part-time adjunct faculty who serve as regular NP preceptors to assist the other students as they care for the shelter patients. With this number of people, we are able to efficiently see as many as 30-40 patients over a 4-hour evening clinic session.

Health Needs of the Homeless— Anecdotes and Lessons

One of my first patients was a somewhat heavyset woman, aged 26, who said she had delivered a baby a week earlier. Her postpartum bleeding was now increasing instead of decreasing. We asked her what happened to the baby and she said "They took it away from me." I felt so sad for her that after the nine months of gestation, after seeing the face of her newborn child for a few days, that the baby would be sent home to someone else. I am not faulting the hospital or the social services. I know they try to make the best decision for the child, but the situation was still heart-rendering for me. We made a referral for this woman to go to the Women's Hospital, a part of the larger Los Angeles County General Hospital, to be examined for follow-up emergency care for her continued hemorrhaging.

In another case, a young couple with gentle and concerned faces, dressed in black leather jackets, came to us. They confided that they were both HIV-positive, but were too frightened to go to any clinics for follow-up care. In the years that I have worked with the homeless, I have learned that people who grow up without regular medical care are often very fearful of health care providers and the health care system. This is obviously a huge barrier to seeking care. We did our best to make the necessary referrals, explain about the implications of their HIV tests, and urge them to go in for treatment. They looked bewildered. I do not know what happened to them after the night we saw them. A permanent shelter clinic, with a nurse available daily, might be able to link people like this to a clinic, perhaps by the nurse accompanying them on their first visit.

A 30-something man came to us nearly every week with large and deep leg ulcers. The ulcers healed slowly because he was an insulin-dependent diabetic. Each time he came to our clinic, we would soak the ulcerated legs, cleanse the wounds, apply antibiotic ointment, and rewrap his legs. With the dressings off, we could see that the ulcers were 1-2 inches deep and at least 3 inches in diameter, exposing his tendons and even the

> People who grow up without regular medical care are often very fearful of health care providers and the health care system.

tibia in some places. The ulcers were lined with the bright pink tissue of his muscles. He told us the ulcers began over a year ago and that he had been hospitalized a couple of times at the County hospital. With rest, good nutrition, and minimal walking around, the ulcers would begin to heal at the hospital. However, lack of funds meant it was not possible for the hospital to keep him as an inpatient long enough for the ulcers to heal completely.

He confided that several doctors recommended amputation, but he said, "I will never let them take off my leg." It appeared to us that he was taking his insulin and trying to manage his diabetes to the best of his ability, but he admitted that it was difficult for him to find the right foods to eat. Life on the streets reduces one's food options to food pantries and soup kitchens where the food is often starchy and comes from bags or cans. Fresh vegetables, high protein foods, and dairy products may be in short supply.

I have encountered the fear of amputation on several occasions while serving homeless people who have foot ulcers. I had another homeless gentleman also tell me he refused amputation. He very candidly told me, "How will I survive as a homeless person without my leg?" His point was that most homeless persons rely heavily on their feet for survival.

Common Medical Problems

The most common problems among the homeless are upper and lower respiratory tract infections. We see everything from the common cold to bronchitis and occasionally acute pneumonia. Those with suspected pneumonia we automatically refer to the hospital emergency department, but those with bronchitis and colds we are able to treat with antibiotics or with over-the-counter medications to ease the symptoms for milder infections. It occurred to me one afternoon, as I was shopping for cold medicines for our clinic, that the simple task of buying cold medicine is beyond most of our homeless clients. Most have so little money that they cannot spare any of it to buy medicine. For some it is logistically not possible for them to purchase medications. Nearly all of our clients express their appreciation for our services, medications, and information we provide.

Other common health problems we see are skin ailments and foot problems. The homeless are subject to environmental hazards such as insect bites, sunburns, scrapes and scratches, and dry cracked skin and lips. Also, since many homeless must travel everywhere on foot, their shoes often wet from rain or dew, their feet are prone to fungal infections, blisters, and maceration (a condition where the skin of the foot turns white and begins to peel from constant wetness). Foot care is a major component of the care we offer. We soak their feet to clean any sores, trim the nails in a safe manner, and provide dressings and clean socks. We also provide foot care products (antifungal medication and foot powder) along with simple written instructions on how to care for one's feet, emphasizing the importance of allowing the feet to dry out completely during the day, wearing clean dry socks daily, and rotating pairs of shoes (if they can possibly afford a second or third pair). We also provide new socks and occasionally new shoes, as well as elastic stockings for those with particularly severe foot/leg problems. If there are extreme problems, we make referrals to a local community health center where the homeless can receive free care.

Musculoskeletal problems (such as strains and sprains), joint problems, and untreated fractures are also common. This is where the FNPs' clinical assessment skills are extremely important. We do not have X-ray available to us, since we are only an outreach clinic, so we must rely on the history that the client tells us, and perform a careful physical examination to distinguish which injuries we can treat with a simple ace wrap and ibuprofen, and which ones we must refer for urgent care. We make a determination as to whether the client must go for care immediately (to the emergency department) or if he or she can wait until morning to go to the community health center.

Chronic Health Problems

Many clients have high blood pressure (some very high, as much as 130 mm Hg diastolic readings) and many have diabetes, in some cases insulin dependent. These are some of our most challenging cases. Since we are not affiliated with a clinical laboratory for baseline lab testing, we are not able to provide antihypertensive medications or diabetes medications. However, we do check blood pressure on all of our clients and we are able to check blood sugars with a glucometer.[5]

Each season we see numerous clients who have mental illness and substance abuse problems. The L.A. County Dept. of Mental Health sends a case worker to the shelter several times a week to identify clients with serious mental illness and encourage them to go in for care. However, many of our mentally ill remain unable to adequately access the care that they need. The few community mental health agencies are overloaded, and the bureaucracy and wait times for care become insurmountable barriers for our clients.

> The bureaucracy and wait times for care become insurmountable barriers for our clients.

The same is true for our clients who have substance abuse problems. Treatment programs for substance abuse are also few and far between. Nevertheless, in our outreach clinic we do our best to provide counseling and referral for mental health problems and substance abuse issues. Occasionally, when these issues become acute at the shelter—such as threatened suicide or violence, or in cases of possible overdose—we have called the police and/or the paramedics. It is a myth that all homeless persons are addicted to alcohol or drugs; statistics reveal that only 40% are burdened with addictions. The addictions act as a type of bondage on these patients. It is not just a simple choice of the client to use or not to use substances (drugs and/or alcohol), but rather it is a compulsion over which they feel powerless. Most are not able to be freed of it without professional help. We readily rely on referrals to Alcoholics Anonymous (AA) and Narcotics Anonymous (NA), who are reported to have about a 50% success rate. These treatment programs function on a 12-step model, originally developed as a Christian approach to addiction recovery. The advantage is that these programs address the spiritual component of addictions.

> *Every human being is created in the image of God and is therefore worthy of our care, our respect, and of being treated with dignity.*

For two seasons, we cared for a 38-year-old gentleman who had had open heart surgery. His surgery had been performed at the county hospital, the finest cardiologists caring for him. He kept all of his clinic appointments and took all of his medications as ordered. Yet, he died within two years of his surgery. It seemed so fruitless that an estimated $50,000 could be spent on his cardiology care, but there was not a single dollar available to help this man find permanent housing. For reasons such as this, we continue to work toward ending homelessness at a socio-political community level.

Conclusion

I hope this article has provided the reader with some insights into the problem of homelessness and health problems of the homeless, and ways in which we have endeavored to bring care to those in our area. The homeless problem continues to grow in most communities, and nurses will be increasingly called upon to serve homeless patients. The better we can understand them and their needs, the better nursing care we will be able to provide them. We must also remember to pray. I recommend that we pray before starting our work, pray for the homeless at church, pray for them as we treat them, and offer prayer (but may they feel comfortable to accept or decline our prayers). I find inspiration in caring for the homeless from the late Mother Theresa. The essence of her teaching is that every human being is created in the image of God and is therefore worthy of our care, our respect, and of being treated with dignity. She also held that Christ often comes to us in disguise; it is up to us to recognize and serve him. We, the faculty and students, who serve in the outreach clinic, appreciate her words to remind us of the real reasons we are there.

QUESTIONS FOR DISCUSSION

1. Why did the author begin her ministry to the homeless? What challenges did she face? What did she find fulfilling about meeting the needs of others in this way?

2. What are the greatest health concerns of homeless individuals in Los Angeles County? Why do you feel they face these challenges? In what ways are their health needs similar to or different than those of the homeless in your area?

3. Professor Brehm and her students gave medical care to individuals who could have paid for such services, had they been more disciplined with their spending in other areas (i.e., no alcohol, tobacco or other unnecessary items). Should these individuals have been given care? Why or why not? Be prepared to defend your views to the group.

4. What are the greatest needs of the homeless in your area? Make a list of their top three concerns and share it with your group. What might be done to meet their needs in these areas?

NOTES

1. We are in the East San Gabriel Valley, an area encompassing 38 small communities along the foothills located between Pasadena on the West and Pomona on the East, or perhaps best described as the northeast corner of Los Angeles County.

2. The closest alternative shelter is 15 miles away, too far for many to travel.

3. She was 14 years old at the time, the eldest of four daughters ages 14, 12, 10, and 8, who were homeless with their father (aged 42). After more than a year of homelessness, this particular family finally found housing with the help of a church, some assistance from county social services, and the girls' father putting in every ounce of effort he had to keep his family together, fed, and clothed. He eventually secured full-time employment.

4. Through our shelter outreach clinic we were able to help Maria find prenatal care. We gave supportive care and visited her when she delivered her baby in a nearby hospital. Her two-year-old son had already been removed from her by social services; at the age of two days her newborn son was taken away, too, before she left the hospital. Maria cried and cried.

Although I personally had called every family shelter and every program that assists pregnant women in Los Angeles County (several days of phone calling) there was no shelter spot or home that could or would accommodate her. They all said they were already full, most saying they get many calls every day, but have no room. When Maria was discharged from the hospital (3 days after her Caesarean section) she was placed in a wheel chair in the hospital lobby late in the afternoon and told she had to leave. She called me, in tears because of losing her infant and having nowhere to go. I intended to take her back to the church shelter for the night, but I thought to myself, "What kind of a Christian am I, if I do not provide a bed for this woman for at least one night in her dire circumstances?" I have a general policy for myself that I do not carry my homeless clients in my car or allow them to come to my office or my home, to avoid personal danger, but this night I made an exception.

It was early January, still the Christmas season, and I had reflected on the holy family of Joseph and Mary who had nowhere to stay when Jesus was born. I am sure that even back then, people around them must certainly have been aware of their need for shelter and that Mary was close to delivery, but only the innkeeper at one place allowed them a spot in a stable for shelter. With my heart convicted by the Christmas story, I felt I had to welcome Maria to my home, at least for just one night. When she came to my house, she smiled as she gazed at my family and our pets. We ate dinner together and I wondered how long it had been since Maria had been in a regular home. It made me realize what a sanctuary a home provides.

The next day a colleague and I paid for a week in a motel for Maria until she recovered from the delivery, though she continued to grieve the loss of her infant. We made visits to her motel to check on her condition during that time. Eventually, she went back to staying in the church shelter.

5. We also provide information on lifestyle and nutrition to assist clients in managing these chronic problems. However, for adequate medicinal treatment we also refer them to the community health center. Over the years, we have developed a cordial working relationship with the East Valley Community Health Center of West Covina, a center that receives federal grant funds to serve the homeless in our area without charge to them. The health center agrees to see our referred clients on an as-needed basis, though the wait is sometimes long. As we give our clients the referral form, we also have them sign a consent for release of information, so that we are able to follow-up and find out which of our clients actually went in for care. From our follow-up statistics, it appears that only about 50% actually make it in to the health center for care. We have come to understand that health care often becomes a lower priority for the homeless, given their struggle for survival.

Ethical Perspectives on Poverty and Health Care

by Joann P. Wessman and Marilyn Chambers

Summary: Pressing ethical questions arise when nurses consider the poor and the adequacy of their health care. Wessman and Chambers present three ethical frameworks, relevant scriptural principles and potential responses for the reader to consider.

How shall I act toward the poor with compromised access to health care? When I am faced with the unmet health care needs of the poor, what kind of a person should I be? Am I intentionally or unintentionally contributing to the poor's societal disadvantage in accessing health care? These ethical questions are professionally urgent, especially for the nurse who bears the name of Jesus Christ. First, we shall look at the underlying ethical perspectives reflected in these questions. Next, we shall identify a few of the passages in Scripture that seem to relate to these questions. We shall conclude with suggesting responses to the unmet needs of the poor, responses appropriate to those in nursing bearing the name of Christ.

> When I am faced with the unmet health care needs of the poor, what kind of a person should I be?

Ethical Frameworks For Viewing Poverty And Health Care

The opening questions reflect three differing frameworks for viewing the needs of the poor within health care. The first question focuses on actions, the second on virtues, and the third on a pattern of oppression toward groups of persons.

Rule Ethics

The first opening question pertains to actions, and reflects the concern of "rule" ethics to act in a manner that maximizes good and minimizes harm. Rule ethics derives from the concerns of the Western European Enlightenment period to determine rationally what action is right through deductive arguments from a given set of rules. Principles often cited to determine how to act, or to justify actions that have

Joann P. Wessman, Ph.D., RN, has been professor of nursing at Bethel University, St. Paul, MN, since 1998, teaching in the generic, degree completion, and graduate nursing programs. In the graduate program she teaches a course on ethics for nursing leaders. Her research is focused on faith-health integration in the church-affiliated elderly.

Marilyn Chambers, MSN, RN, serves as adjunct faculty of nursing at Bethel. She owns a home health care consulting firm. In addition she serves in the Air Force Reserve where she holds the rank of colonel. With Dr. Wessman, she is involved in research on faith-health integration in the church-affiliated elderly and parish nursing.

been taken, include nonmaleficence, beneficence, respect for autonomy, justice, truth-telling, confidentiality, utility, and promise-keeping, among others. The ANA 1985 Code of Ethics uses basic moral principles to "prescribe and justify nursing actions." The clear emphasis is on behavior, the rightness of what I do as a nurse. Health care ethics committees often use rule ethics to determine the appropriate action in a given complex clinical situation. Rule ethics is perhaps the approach most commonly experienced by the nurse in the study of ethics.

One common way that we see the application of rule ethics is in procuring informed consent. A patient is presented with the benefits (principle of beneficence) and risks (principle of nonmaleficence) of a procedure before giving consent for a procedure or surgery to be done. Another example is the principle of the patient's right to confidentiality. This standard of confidentiality reflects general principles (or rules) that are presumed to be right.

Within rule ethics are two approaches to looking at the rightness of an action. Jeremy Bentham and John Stuart Mill focused on the consequences of an action. A given action is "right" if it produces the desired consequences. An action that increases access of the poor to health care and limits unpleasant consequences for others attempting to access health care would be deemed appropriate. This general approach of justifying the means by end results is called utilitarianism. Its principle of utility looks for means to achieve the greatest good for the greatest numbers of people.

In contrast, Immanuel Kant held that some actions are intrinsically right or wrong, separate from the end results that may be achieved. Kant proposed that some actions are always wrong, even if through these actions, good may be achieved in a given context. For Kant, motives were

important indicators of right or wrong action. Actions embedded in a sense of duty, reflective of respect for every person as a rational being, and universally appropriate would be deemed "right." Actions that violate a principle such as truth-telling always would be wrong, regardless of the good that might be achieved through a false statement. Rightness is a function of the act, not of the consequences resulting from the act.

Both branches of rule ethics look at the rightness of the actions a nurse takes when she or he becomes aware of persons in need of health care whose poverty bars them from access to services.

Virtue Ethics

What kind of a person ought I to be? What kind of a community should we be? These questions focus on the *character* of the nurse and nursing community confronting the unmet needs of the poor for health care. *Virtues* to be reflected by the nurse or nursing community become the

---

ETHICAL FRAMEWORKS FOR VIEWING POVERTY AND HEALTH CARE

Rule Ethics

Virtue Ethics

Ethics with a Focus on Oppression of Vulnerable Groups

---

focus. Character is primary; behavior is secondary. Appropriate behavior flows from good character.

This approach to ethics has roots in antiquity—Plato, Aristotle, Buddhistic moral theory, Confucianism, and Taoism, among others (Volbrecht 2002, 96). This was the focus of ethical decision making in the early history of nursing in this country (Aikens 1916).

A focus on virtue ethics is more evident in the current ANA Code for Nurses than in prior versions of the code. Volbrecht (2002) offers a list of nursing virtues that constitute "good character." She lists compassion, fidelity to trust, moral courage, justice, mediation, self-confidence, resilience, practical reasoning, and integrity. Dr. Volbrecht suggests that moral character is developed and sustained within the nursing community through mentoring and co-mentoring involving immersion in the context of practice, imitation of good models, and ongoing critical reflection (119). She notes that the primary context for mentoring must be within nursing practice.

> What kind of a person ought I to be? What kind of a community should we be?

Examples of virtue ethics readily come to mind. We expect a nurse to be compassionate, and when she or he is not so, we feel violated. Or, we expect a nurse to act for the good of the client. When a nurse's attitude seems to say, "what's in it for me?" we feel repulsed. Both examples speak to virtues that we commonly believe are to be a part of the character of the nurse. On an organizational level, we commonly see the *values* of a health care organization publicly displayed. These values reflect virtues that the organization commits to exemplify in all its processes.

We note with dismay the larger-sized clinical laboratory groups in nursing education that often force faculty to focus on client physical safety, not on critical reflection with the student on her/his emerging nursing character. We also feel concern at the busy, understaffed acute care settings that again force the new graduate to focus on doing, not on being.

Ethics with a Focus on Oppression of Vulnerable Groups

This ethical framework is not as clearly defined as the first two discussed. It borrows from feminine ethics; it reflects some of the themes of liberation theology. "Good" is seen as that which empowers every person—regardless of gender, age, social status, racial/ethical origin, or economic resources—to become whole, to live in health, to make appropriate health care choices. "Evil" is any kind of systematic external oppression that renders groups of persons disadvantaged in seeking health and health care.

The framework embodies characteristics of both rule and virtue ethics. *Consequences* of actions are viewed in terms of directly or indirectly contributing to oppression. Societal, health care, and individual provider *attitudes* are examined for barriers to health care access for the poor. Unfavorable actions and attitudes become tools of oppression to deny the poor proper access to services.

This school of ethics holds the basic ideas that subordination of any person or group is morally wrong, oppressive imbalances of power must be eliminated, and voices of the poor must be heard in crafting health care policy. The focus is on both individual and societal consequences of actions and on attitudes. Coalition building, partnerships, advocacy, and community involvement are concepts interrelated in seeking to eliminate oppression.

Poverty And Access To Health Care Viewed Through Scripture

Scripture is filled with principles prescribing how we should treat the poor (rule ethics) and with examples of virtue or personal qualities that reflect a righteous character in relating with the poor (virtue ethics). Oppression of the poor in any form is loudly decried.

Principles for Actions toward the Poor (Rule Ethics)

Several passages in the Old Testament

law include rules aimed at eliminating poverty. Exodus 23:10-11 gives us an example of right action; God commanded the Israelites for six years to "sow your fields and harvest the crops, but during the seventh year let the land lie unplowed and unused. Then the poor among your people may get food from it..." God made provision for the poor out of the bounty of the land.

In Leviticus 19:9-10, God gave the directive for landowners to leave the corners of the field unharvested and not to go over the vineyards a second time. The over-

> When you reap the harvest of your land, do not reap to the very edges of your field or gather the gleanings of your harvest. Do not go over your vineyard a second time or pick up the grapes that have fallen. Leave them for the poor and the alien. I am the LORD your God.
> Leviticus 19:9-10 (NIV)

looked grain and grapes were for the poor and the alien. The landowner had a responsibility to leave some of the harvest for those who had no land. It was not the first or greatest portion that had to be given, but what was left on the edges. Even a small amount of grain or grapes was acceptable. While it is most likely that the choicest grains and grapes were harvested first, the remainder still was of good quality and nutritious.

We can draw the conclusion that every offering is of value. In health care, this principle might be illustrated in giving basic care. Nursing is strong in the traditions of providing comfort, listening, educating, respecting each person, and supporting the person in attaining his or her highest level of health, as he or she defines it. In today's health care environment, it can feel as though there is not enough time or resources to make a difference. However, every offering of care counts.

Leviticus 25:8-10 identifies how God decreed a year of Jubilee—the 50th year after seven Sabbath years, or 49 years. At this time, sold property returned to the original family line and slaves returned to their families. Debts were erased; a clean slate was established. The poverty of one generation was not passed down to subsequent generations. While certain exceptions were made for property in walled cities and for Levites, the general rule was that property reverted to the original owners. Thus, a provision was made to prevent generational poverty.

In health care today, we see how poverty becomes a generational concern. As immigrants and refugees come to this country, they encounter nurses in facilities and services often at the "margins." We see stigma and shame. The above Scriptures suggest the need to address basic health care needs and to prevent generational compromised access to health care.

The New Testament Scriptures commend actions that value each person regardless of status or income. In that culture, those with wealth and power were given much honor and consideration. The poor and those of lower status were devalued. Beginning with the Beatitudes in Matthew 5, Jesus sharply contradicts the standard

> The King will reply, "I tell you the truth, whatever you did for one of the least of these brothers of mine, you did for me."
> Matthew 25:40 (NIV)

view that only the wealthy and influential had God's blessing. In Matthew 25:34-45 Jesus declares that what was done or not done for the needy is of eternal consequence. He makes a direct connection between serving the needy and serving Jesus himself. Those who did not serve the needy also were not serving Jesus.

In the story of the Good Samaritan,

Luke 10:25-37, Jesus clearly spoke that whoever sees someone in need is to respond with generosity. In this account, the Samaritan has no personal knowledge of the injured man, did not know anything of the circumstances of the injury, did not know if this was a real situation or a trap, and did not appear to have any interest in the outcome. He saw a need, had the ability to do something, and acted.

James 2:14-17 addresses faith and deeds toward the poor. "What good is it, my brothers, if a man claims to have faith but has no deeds? Can such faith save him? Suppose a brother or sister is without clothes and daily food. If one of you says to him, 'Go, I wish you well; keep warm and well fed,' but does nothing about his physical needs, what good is it? In the same way, faith by itself, if it is not accompanied by action, is dead." Faith—yes! But right actions toward the poor also are required.

Virtue or Personal Qualities That Reflect Righteous Character (Virtue Ethics)

Numerous passages throughout Scripture speak of character formed through identification with Christ, out of which flows righteous actions towards the poor. One such passage is the Beatitudes. Blessed are those whose character reflects virtues such as humility, mercy, purity of heart, peace making, and ability to withstand pressure. The fruits of the Spirit recorded in Galatians 5:22 reflect other character traits of the righteous person: love, joy, peace, patience, kindness, generosity, faithfulness, gentleness, and self-control.

Oppression

Scripture as a whole severely decries oppression and promises that it will not go unnoticed. God heard the groaning of the Hebrew people in Egypt and acted to free the slaves. God brought great calamity to the oppressor—the ten plagues that resulted in great loss of life and destruction. Numerous Old Testament prophets cried out against oppression of the poor in Israel and Judah. They testified that God's anger is aroused because of idolatry and oppression. These behaviors ultimately led to exile from the Promised Land. In James 2, the apostle warns against attitudes of partiality that favor the rich over the poor in the assembly. Partiality, he identifies, is sin.

Responses To Unmet Health Care Needs Of The Poor

Three questions may guide the Christian nurse in forging an ethical response to the unmet needs of the poor in accessing health care:

Right Actions

Right actions are suggested both by the review of rule ethics and in Scripture. We must not do harm to the poor within health care systems, such as subjecting them to

> • What can I do (actions) to contribute to a reasonable and just health care system that meets the needs of the poor?
>
> • What qualities (virtues) do I need to affirm, both personally and organizationally, in serving the poor?
>
> • How can I respond prophetically to patterns of oppression of the poor within the health care system?

long delays to receive basic care. We should pursue actions that bring about timely access to care (beneficence). We must protect the autonomy of the poor person to make health care decisions; we must not act in a paternalistic manner. We must not compromise the telling of truth, regardless of the socioeconomic status of the care recipient. We must keep promises and protect confidentiality.

We must find ways to provide basic care for all persons. To serve the poor is to serve Christ. To reach as "Good Samaritans" across artificially created barriers to provide care to the poor is a scriptural mandate, not negotiable option.

At times our actions will be directed toward poor individuals needing care. We see a need, and act to meet that need. Perhaps we are led to volunteer at clinics serving the poor, or perhaps we find ways through our churches to provide direct services. At other times, we act to address injustices within our health care agency like language barriers, vocabulary difficulty levels, or cumbersome policies that create unnecessary "red tape." We serve on agency committees to improve health care access for the poor. We engage political processes to change local and national health care policy. We advocate on behalf of the poor and form coalitions to better provide better health care access for the poor.

Right Character (Virtues)

What qualities do I need to develop in order to serve the poor in a righteous manner? Volbrecht's list mentioned earlier provides a starting place—particularly compassion, fidelity to trust, moral courage, resilience, and integrity. The qualities embedded in the Beatitudes and fruits of the Spirit suggest how our character is to be formed in Christ. These qualities spring from our relationship with Christ and are reflected in our nursing practice. My Christian character should be a part of my organizational behaviors. I should be salt and light within my agency, encouraging righteous behaviors toward the poor. I must model righteous character.

I need to see myself as a member of a community, first the community of faith, and then the health care community. I need to foster relationships that build good character within my employing agency. I may need to reach out to a young professional nurse who

is overwhelmed. I may need to have the moral courage to confront unacceptable practices. I may need to be resilient after what felt like a battering.

Prophetic Voice Against Oppression

How can I respond prophetically to patterns of oppression of the poor within the health care system? First, I need to look at the consequences of my behaviors, intended or unintended. Likewise, I need to look at the consequences of agency behaviors. Are our consent forms written in a manner that assures autonomy of decision making? Do I need to suggest revisions? What other barriers reflect unethical practices when held up to the standard of "do no harm"? Do I need to speak out against contracts that discount services for the insured, but charge full price to the uninsured?

> Scripture as a whole severely decries oppression and promises that it will not go unnoticed.

How can I give voice to the poor who have been barred from participating in health care access decisions? Do I need to suggest that the voice of the poor be added to ethics committees and to commissions seeking to guide public health care policy? What opportunities do I have to become a voice against oppression? These are questions that I must ask if I would become an ethical prophetic voice on behalf of the poor.

Conclusion

Ethical principles embedded in Scripture guide the nurse to minister in a righteous manner in meeting the health care needs of the poor. Right actions springing from righteous character bring about right results. Confronting oppressive practices within the health care system and giving voice to the oppressed poor are powerful ways for the nurse to act ethically.

QUESTIONS FOR DISCUSSION

1. Consider the material presented regarding rule ethics, principles for actions toward the poor, and right actions. Describe an actual or fictitious situation in health care among the poor where these concepts might be applied.

2. Consider the material presented regarding virtue ethics, virtue or personal qualities that reflect righteous character, and right character.

    a. Describe an actual or fictitious situation where a nurse or health care worker demonstrated positive character traits in working with the poor. What difference did this character trait make in the lives of both the nurse and the person served?

    b. Identify two character qualities you would like to develop more fully in yourself.

3. Consider the material presented regarding a focus on oppression of vulnerable groups, Scripture regarding oppression and the prophetic voice against oppression.

    a. Describe an actual or fictitious scenario where the poor are oppressed. What are some ways nurses can act together, united in their profession, to respond to oppression?

    b. What are some ways you personally can be a voice for the poor?

REFERENCES

Aikens, C. A. 1916. *Studies in ethics for nurses.* Philadelphia: W. B. Saunders Company.

Bilynskyj, S. S. 1987. *Christian ethics and the ethics of virtue.* Chicago: Covenant Publications. http://www.efn.org/~ssb/papers/virtue.htm (retrieved January 19, 2005).

Glaser, J. W., and Hamel, R. P., eds. 1997. *Three realms of managed care: Societal, institutional, individual.* Kansas City: Sheed & Ward.

Larson, V. n.d. A feminist ethic of care and God's words of care. http://www.vow.org/feminism/contemporary.issues/xxxxxxx-vlarson-feminist_ethic_of_care.html (retrieved January 19, 2005).

Rhodes, R. 1991. Christian revolution in Latin America: The changing face of liberation theology. http://home.earthlink.net/~ronrhodes/Liberation.html (retrieved January 24, 2005).

Sider, R. J. 1980. An evangelical theology of liberation. http://www.religion-online.org/showarticle.asp?title-1757 (retrieved January 24, 2005).

Volbrecht, R. M. 2002. *Nursing ethics: communities in dialogue.* Upper Saddle River, NJ: Prentice Hall.

LEARNING ACTIVITIES

Compassion vs. Laziness: The Bible and The Poor

The Bible contains numerous verses that cry out for justice and mercy for the poor, command protection for the weak and vulnerable, and call for people to care for and provide for the needs of the poor. There are also verses that praise the value of diligent work, disapprove of laziness, and describe the negative consequences of idleness.

Read the Bible verses below. After dividing into groups, read and compare the following verses, using the questions below to guide your discussion.

DISCUSSION QUESTIONS

1. What differences do you notice between the verses in the two sections below? How would you explain the tension, or seeming contradiction, between them?

2. Who are these verses describing?

3. What, if anything, surprised you about these verses?

4. Choose one verse from each section and describe a situation where the chosen verse might apply.

5. Can you think of a time in your own life or work when one of these verses applied?

6. How would you summarize what these verses say regarding how we are to treat the poor?

BIBLE VERSES: *Justice & Mercy for the Poor*

"For I was hungry and you gave me something to eat, I was thirsty and you gave me something to drink, I was a stranger and you invited me in, I needed clothes and you clothed me, I was sick and you looked after me, I was in prison and you came to visit me.' The King will reply, 'I tell you the truth, whatever you did for one of the least of these brothers of mine, you did for me.'" Matthew 25: 35-36, 40

"Speak up for those who cannot speak for themselves, for the rights of all who are destitute. Speak up and judge fairly; defend the rights of the poor and needy." Proverbs 31:8-9

"If anyone has material possessions and sees his brother in need but has no pity on him, how can the love of God be in him? Dear children, let us not love with words or tongue but with actions and in truth." 1 John 3: 17-18

"Is not this the kind of fasting I have chosen: to loose the chains of injustice and untie the cords of the yoke, to set the oppressed free and break every yoke? Is it not to share your food with the hungry and to provide the poor wanderer with shelter- when you see the naked, to clothe him, and not to turn away from your own flesh and blood? ...If you spend yourselves in behalf of the hungry and satisfy the needs of the oppressed, then your light will rise in the darkness, and your night will become like the noonday. The LORD will guide you always." Isaiah 58: 9b-11

"What good is it, my brothers, if a man claims to have faith but has no deeds? Can such faith save him? Suppose a brother or sister is without clothes and daily food. If one of you says to him, 'Go, I wish you well; keep warm and well fed,' but does nothing about his physical needs, what good is it? In the same way, faith by itself, if it is not accompanied by action, is dead." James 2: 14-17

"Suppose a man comes into your meeting wearing a gold ring and fine clothes, and a poor man in shabby clothes also comes in. If you show special attention to the man wearing fine clothes and say, 'Here's a good seat for you,' but say to the poor man, 'You stand there' or 'Sit on the floor by my feet,' have you not discriminated among yourselves and become judges with evil thoughts? Listen, my dear brothers: Has not God chosen those who are poor in the eyes of the world to be rich in faith and to inherit the kingdom he promised those who love him? But you have insulted the poor. Is it not the rich who are exploiting you?" James 2: 1-7

"Learn to do right! Seek justice, encourage the oppressed. Defend the cause of the fatherless, plead the case of the widow." Isaiah 1:17

"He who oppresses the poor shows contempt for their Maker, but whoever is kind to the needy honors God...If a man shuts his ears to the cry of the poor, he too will cry out and not be answered." Proverbs 14:31; Proverbs 21:13

"My whole being will exclaim, 'Who is like you, O LORD? You rescue the poor from those too strong for them, the poor and needy from those who rob them '" Psalm 35:10

"There will always be poor people in the land. Therefore I command you to be open-handed toward your brothers and toward the poor and needy in your land." Deuteronomy 15:11

BIBLE VERSES: *Values of Diligent Work*
"The plans of the diligent lead to profit as surely as haste leads to poverty." Proverbs 21:55

"For even when we were with you, we gave you this rule: 'If a man will not work, he shall not eat.' We hear that some among you are idle. They are not busy; they are busybodies. Such people we command and urge in the Lord Jesus Christ to settle down and earn the bread they eat." 2 Thessalonians 3: 10-12

"I went past the field of the sluggard, past the vineyard of the man who lacks judgment; thorns had come up everywhere, the ground was covered with weeds, and the stone wall was in ruins. I applied my heart to what I observed and learned a lesson from what I saw: A little sleep, a little slumber, a little folding of the hands to rest- and poverty will come on you like a bandit and scarcity like an armed man." Proverbs 24:30-34

"Go to the ant, you sluggard; consider its ways and be wise! It has no commander, no overseer or ruler, yet it stores its provisions in summer and gathers its food at harvest. How long will you lie there, you sluggard? When will you get up from your sleep?" Proverbs 6: 6-9

"Make it your ambition to lead a quiet life, to mind your own business and to work with your hands, just as we told you, so that your daily life may win the respect of outsiders and so that you will not be dependent on anybody." 1 Thess. 4: 11-12

"You yourselves know that these hands of mine have supplied my own needs and the needs of my companions. In everything I did, I showed you that by this kind of hard work we must help the weak, remembering the words the Lord Jesus himself said: 'It is more blessed to give than to receive.'" Acts 20:34-35

"The sluggard buries his hand in the dish; he is too lazy to bring it back to his mouth." Proverbs 26:15

"A wife of noble character who can find? She is worth far more than rubies. Her husband has full confidence in her and lacks nothing of value…She selects wool and flax and works with eager hands…She gets up while it is still dark; she provides food for her family and portions for her servant girls….She sets about her work vigorously; her arms are strong for her tasks. Proverbs 31: 10-11, 13, 15

RESOURCES

WEBSITES

Bread for the World: http://www.bread.org/index.html

Bureau of Labor Statistics; U.S. Department of Labor: http://www.bls.gov/

Call to Renewal: http://www.calltorenewal.com/

Catholic Relief Services: http://www.catholicrelief.org/

Center on Budget and Policy Priorities: http://www.cbpp.org/

Center on Hunger and Poverty; Brandeis University: http://www.centeronhunger.org

Christian Community Health Fellowship: http://www.cchf.org/

Evangelicals for Social Action: http://esa-online.org/

Henry J. Kaiser Family Foundation: http://www.kff.org/

Heritage Foundation, Policy Research and Analysis: http://heritage.org/

Income, Poverty, and Health Insurance Coverage in the United States: 2003;
U.S. Census Bureau: http://www.census.gov/prod/2004pubs/p60-226.pdf

International Council of Nurses: http://www.icn.ch/

Joint Center for Poverty Research: http://www.jcpr.org/

Lawndale Christian Health Center: http://www.lawndale.org/default.htm

Mennonite Central Committee: http://www.mennonitecc.ca/

Minority Health; American Public Health Association:
http://www.apha.org/public_health/minority.htm

National Center for Policy Analysis: http://www.ncpa.org/

National Coalition for the Homeless: http://www.nationalhomeless.org/

National Governor's Association Center for Best Practices: http://www.nga.org/center/

Office of Minority Health; Centers for Disease Control and Prevention:
http://www.cdc.gov/omh/default.htm

Outreach International: http://www.outreach-international.org/

Oxfam America: http://www.oxfamamerica.org

Population Reference Bureau: http://www.prb.org/

Poverty Resource Guide; Eldis: http://www.eldis.org/poverty/index.htm

Poverty; U.S. Census Bureau: http://www.census.gov/hhes/www/poverty.html

Robert Wood Johnson Foundation: http://www.rwjf.org/index.jsp

United States Department of Health & Human Services: http://www.hhs.gov/

US Census Bureau: http://www.census.gov/

World Bank Group: http://www.worldbank.org/

World Factbook; CIA: http://www.cia.gov/cia/publications/factbook/

World Health Organization: http://www.who.int/en/

RECOMMENDED READINGS

Anderson, E. 1999. *Code of the Street.* New York: W. W. Norton & Company, Inc.

Gordon, W. 1995. *Real Hope in Chicago.* Grand Rapids: Zondervan.

Iceland, J. 2003. *Poverty in America: A handbook.* Berkeley: University of California Press.

Kim, J. Y., J. V. Millen, A. Irwin, and J. Gershman, eds. 2000. *Dying for growth: Global inequality and the health of the poor.* Monroe, ME: Common Courage Press.

Leininger, M. M. 1991. *Culture, Care, Diversity & Universality: A Theory of Nursing.* New York: National League for Nursing Press.

Leon, D., and W. Gill, eds. 2001. *Poverty, Inequality, and Health.* New York: Oxford UP.

Lipson, J. G., S. L. Dibble, and P. A. Minarik. 1996. *Culture and Nursing Care: A Pocket Guide.* San Fransisco: UCSF Nursing Press.

Masson, V. 2001. *Ninth Street Notebook: Voice of a nurse in the city.* Washington, D.C.: Sage Femme Press.

Payne, R. 2001. *A framework for understanding poverty.* Highlands, TX: aha! Process, Inc.

Payne, R., P. DeVol, and T. D. Smith. 2001. *Bridges out of poverty: Strategies for professionals and communities.* Highlands, TX: aha! Process, Inc.

Shipler, D. K. 2004. *The working poor: Invisible in America.* New York: Knopf.

Sider, R. 1997. *Rich Christians in an age of hunger: Moving from affluence to generosity.* Anniv. ed. Nashville: W. Publishing Group.

Volbrecht, R. M. 2002. *Nursing ethic: communities in dialogue.* Upper Saddle River, NJ: Prentice Hall.

NOTES

NOTES